WHEELED ARMOURED FIGHTING VEHICLES

IN SERVICE

B. T. White

WHEELED ARMOURED FIGHTING VEHICLES

IN SERVICE

Illustrated by
Peter Sarson and Tony Bryan

BLANDFORD PRESS
POOLE · DORSET

First published in the U.K. 1983 by Blandford Press,
Link House, West Street, Poole, Dorset, BH15 1LL.

Copyright © 1983 Blandford Books Ltd.

Distributed in the United States by
Sterling Publishing Co., Inc.,
2 Park Avenue, New York, N.Y. 10016.

British Library Cataloguing in Publication Data

White, B. T.
    Wheeled armoured fighting vehicles in service.
    1. Armoured vehicles, Military
    I. Title
    623.74'75   UG446.5

ISBN 0 7137 1022 5

Typeset by Polyglot Pte Ltd

Printed in Italy by Interlitho, Milan

Contents

6

The publishers wish to thank Mr Christopher Foss for his kind help in supplying many of the photographs for the book. Thanks are also due to the many manufacturers who provided photographs of their products.

Preface

This book offers a selection of some of the most important and interesting wheeled armoured vehicles in service today. The choice is entirely the author's and has to some extent been dictated by the availability of information and/or suitable reference material for the illustrations.

They are grouped according to the country of design of the basic vehicle. In most cases this also means the country of manufacture, but where design and manufacture are shared between two countries this is recognised in the headings and the illustration captions of the vehicles concerned.

The vehicles are shown in typical colour schemes for the countries using them. Completely accurate reproduction of colours in a book of this kind is extremely difficult, and in any case the colours used on the vehicles vary widely, but some notes on camouflage schemes as used in different countries are contained in the book.

In order to supplement the written descriptions of the interior layouts of wheeled armoured vehicles, a few section views of representative types are included. The vehicles shown here are, in several cases, prototypes rather than production models, since up-to-date and fully detailed interior views of current types are rarely released for publication.

Tabulated data on the majority of vehicles described is also included at the back of the book. This should be taken as a rough comparative guide only for several reasons, one being that fully reliable data is not available for all countries; another is that manufacturers' data, used in many cases, will no longer apply where vehicles are modified in service, as they so often are.

Many sources of information have been used in the compilation of this book, including manufacturers, government departments, books and journals. Of the latter, *AFV News* and *Tankette*, published by A.F.V. modelling enthusiasts in Canada and England respectively, and containing a wealth of useful information, should receive special mention.

Friends have again assisted in various ways, including Colonel Robert J. Icks whose kind and patient help has been provided over so many years. The author would like to express his grateful thanks to all concerned.

B. T. White
London, 1983

Introduction

Wheeled armoured vehicles are capable of performing most of the tasks of tracked vehicles and for many functions they are, arguably, more suitable. The main advantages of wheeled vehicles over tracked vehicles are that they are simpler to handle, they have lower maintenance costs, are more economical to operate, are generally quieter and faster and can usually be made amphibious more readily.

Wheeled vehicles are not suitable as main battle tanks or self-propelled mountings for heavy guns where a good cross-country performance is needed because their tyres and suspension are not well adapted for weights much above 20 tons and do not provide a good gun platform without the aid of jacks. Apart from this, modern wheeled vehicles can be given a cross-country performance comparable to that of tanks, usually by using a multi-wheeled layout (6×6 or 8×8) and independent suspension. It should be mentioned, however, that the mechanical complexity of multi-wheeled all-wheel-drive vehicles can almost equal that of tracked vehicles, and the transmission noise can be considerable.

Where only road or modest cross-country performance is needed, such as in urban internal security operations, the wheeled armoured vehicle is undoubtedly superior to a tank or other tracked vehicle from nearly every point of view.

These characteristics result in wheeled armoured vehicles being used in three main roles, namely reconnaissance, personnel carrying and internal security, as well as a variety of ancilliary tasks.

Reconnaissance was one of the earliest functions of wheeled armoured vehicles. Once the superiority of the tracked armoured vehicle — the tank — had been established in the main battlefield on the Western Front in World War 1, armoured cars were used in other areas where their range of operation was not inhibited by trench and barbed wire systems. Armoured cars were usefully employed, for instance, in the Arabian desert and on the Eastern Front.

In World War 2 the British and German forces were leading exponents of the use of armoured cars for reconnaissance, the former much more extensively than any other country. The separate approaches of the two countries reflect different points of view on the requirements for an armoured reconnaissance car that are still largely valid today. The best German vehicles in this class were the SdKfz 231 and 234 series, which were mechanically sophisticated 8 × 8 vehicles with a very good cross-country performance, but weighing about 9 tons and being 5.82 metres long. The British Daimler, acknowledged as the best British armoured car of its era, weighed only $7\frac{1}{2}$ tons and was a compact 4 × 4 vehicle with an advanced, for its time, transmission and independent suspension system. These two types of car — German and British — epitomise the conflicting demands on a reconnaissance vehicle for a high degree of cross-country mobility and inconspicuousness, with protection and armament following behind. The West German Luchs on the one hand and the British Fox on the other are lineal descendents of their wartime ancestors, both highly successful in their different ways. Protection on reconnaissance vehicles rarely goes beyond that needed against weapons of up to about 30-mm calibre and shell splinters, since not even main battle tanks can be fully protected against shaped-charge projectiles.

Armament for wheeled reconnaissance vehicles, apart from machine guns, tends to be automatic guns of 20 to 30 mm, although low velocity guns of calibres between 76 and 105 mm firing shaped-charge projectiles of high performance do not impose excessive strains on relatively light chassis. The British Saladin, now superseded in the British Army by Fox and tracked vehicles for reconnaissance, has a 76-mm gun and France has produced a full range of powerfully-armed wheeled vehicles, from the EBR 75 of 1948 and the small AML H-90 with 90-mm gun, to the AMX-10RC with its 105-mm gun.

Anti-tank guided missiles are increasingly being added to the armoury of reconnaissance vehicles, both for self-protection against heavy armoured vehicles and for supporting battle tanks in the assault.

The layout of armoured reconnaissance cars varies, but the most popular configuration is with the driving compartment at the front, the fighting compartment in the middle and the engine at the rear, as typified by such different vehicles as the British Fox, German Luchs and Soviet BRDM-2.

Reconnaissance vehicles need to be able to cross inland waterways and the ability to do so varies from a permanent amphibious capability without preparation and a good speed in water driven by hydro-jets or propellors (such as the German Luchs and Soviet BRDM), to that provided by a simple addition such as the flotation screen on the British Fox, and water propulsion at a modest speed by means of the road wheels. The ability to drive backwards quickly to withdraw from a sudden encounter with the enemy is recognised as an important asset in a reconnaissance vehicle, but the German Luchs and the French EBR 75 are among the few current vehicles which provide a second driver to secure the maximum performance in this respect.

Personnel carrying has been a function of wheeled armoured vehicles from their earliest days. Lorry chassis with a very limited off-road performance were armoured for this purpose during the early days of World War 1. During World War 2, Germany and (to a lesser extent) the United States made extensive use of half-tracked vehicles as armoured personnel carriers. The half-track, which combines some of the advantages (and disadvantages) of wheeled and tracked vehicles, has not been much in vogue since World War 2, probably because a similar or better performance is now attainable with multi-wheeled vehicles. The Israelis have, however, managed to maintain in service large numbers of American half-tracks built during World War 2 and a modified German design was used by Czechoslovakia at least well into the 1970s.

Armoured personnel carriers of the 1980s are nearly all infantry fighting vehicles (I.F.V.s), rather than mere 'battle taxis'. Firing ports from which the passengers can use their personal weapons are usually provided on at least three sides of the vehicle and there is in most cases a mounting or turret for a machine gun or cannon for all-round fire.

The most common layout for an armoured personnel carrier is with the engine at the front, leaving the rear compartment unobstructed, and having a large door or doors at the rear. Doors at both sides are a feature on many A.P.C.s, enabling personnel to disembark on the side sheltered from enemy fire. This feature is particularly important in A.P.C.s or internal security vehicles involved in urban incidents where there is little room for manoeuvre.

Internal security was also an early function of wheeled armoured vehicles, French Hotchkiss armoured cars being used in the Young Turks' rising in Istanbul in 1909 for example. Standard armoured reconnaissance cars and armoured personnel carriers have been and no doubt will continue to be used for internal security purposes. However, specialised vehicles have appeared in recent years which, although in some cases modified versions of military vehicles, have such features as permanent armoured glass windscreens for better observation in urban antiguerilla operations, sometimes with wire grilles for extra protection. Many countries have water cannon (high pressure hoses) mounted on armoured (or unarmoured) vehicles for use against rioters; the East German SK-2 (included in this book) is typical. Special attachments, such as bulldozer blades or similar devices for clearing street obstacles, are available for some vehicles. It has been recognised that internal security vehicles intended for use in urban anti-guerilla activities need thicker armour, since they are likely to encounter small-arms fire at close range, and special protection against inflammable missiles. In other respects a simpler type of vehicle, such as the British Shorland without independent suspension, similar to an earlier generation of armoured reconnaissance cars, is quite suitable.

Wheeled armoured vehicles for what are called here ancilliary purposes — although some are, in fact, prime functions — are a varied group. Missile carriers/launchers are an important class, particularly for the Soviet Union, where wheeled vehicles have replaced tracked vehicles in many instances, even for heavy rockets. Adaptations of light reconnaissance or scout cars, such as the Soviet BRDM or British Ferret, are generally used as carriers for anti-tank missiles, although anti-aircraft and strategic missiles, such as the French Crotale or the Soviet SA-8 Gecko and SS-12 Scaleboard, usually employ special chassis because of the greater complexity of their sys-

tems. Radar carriers often have similar chassis to those of the weapons they serve.

Armoured command, ambulance, and cargo vehicles often have similar hulls to personnel carriers, only the internal fittings being removed or modified to provide the space needed to accommodate a commander's radio sets and other equipment, or stretchers, or an open hold for cargo.

Infantry mortar carriers, from which the mortar can be fired either from inside or outside the vehicle, are usually closely similar to armoured personnel carriers, since the mortar teams are normally an integral part of the infantry unit. Repair vehicles, likewise, are often on the same chassis as the vehicles of the unit they serve.

Manufacturers in many countries are developing 'families' of armoured wheeled vehicles, having some or all of such common factors as the same engine (or different engines from the same engine maker's range); similar automotive components (such as transmission and suspension, whether for 4 × 4, 6 × 6 or 8 × 8 vehicles); similar basic hull design; and similar armament (whether main or subsidiary). A number of common features can also be shared by wheeled and tracked vehicles, as demonstrated by the British CVR(W) and CVR(T) (Fox and Scorpion families) series and the French AMX-10 wheeled and tracked models. A reduction in the number and variety of spares needed is an advantage in any army, and the offer of a range of closely related vehicles to cover many functions is an asset in exporting military vehicles, particularly to less-developed countries.

A very high degree of standardised layout does have some disadvantages; for instance, a rear engine configuration suitable for an armoured reconnaissance car does not necessarily provide the best arrangement for an armoured personnel carrier for which large rear doors are an asset. All armoured vehicles are a compromise, however, and manufacturers, purchasers and users have to decide where their priorities lie.

Armoured Vehicle Camouflage Colours and Markings

The notes which follow give some guidance on the camouflage colours and vehicle markings used by the countries represented in this book. It must be emphasised that accurate colour representation in a book is extremely difficult and that even on a vehicle the appearance of a colour can vary widely according to the state of the light. Colour standards are frequently variable even when newly applied and can in any case alter after ageing and weathering. What is called olive drab here is used as a standard shade by many countries and although it varies between emphasis on brown or green, it tends after a time to end up looking the same for most countries.

Few countries seem able to enforce completely uniform standards for tactical and other markings of vehicles, but some of the more common versions are mentioned below. A marking common to most countries of the world is a red cross for ambulances (red crescent in Moslem countries) and all the NATO countries have a standardised bridge group marking (to indicate the class of bridge the vehicle can cross) which is a black number on a yellow disc carried at the front.

Belgium: overall olive drab. Vehicle registration numbers are in black, preceded by a small black, yellow and red rectangle on a white plate.

Brazil: single colour (e.g. sand) and multi-colour schemes have been used on Brazilian armoured cars, some of which are evidently for the benefit of overseas buyers.

Canada: overall olive drab with additions where necessary to suit terrain, e.g. a high proportion of white added for winter snow operations.

Czechoslovakia: olive drab, although a multi-tone disruptive camouflage system has been known. Vehicle registration plates are black with yellow numerals. The Czech national sign (circle in red, white and blue segments) seems often to be used in the field as well as on parades.

Egypt: normally plain sand yellow overall, sometimes with a disruptive pattern of another colour, but striped camouflage schemes of black, sand and green or other colours have been used, presumably for areas other than desert terrain.

France: overall olive drab normally. Gendarmerie-Nationale riot control vehicles are light blue. Vehicle registration numbers, preceded by a blue, white and red tricolour (with superimposed gold grenade for Gendarmerie and stylised wings for Armee de l'Air vehicles) are in white on a black plate. Regimental badges and individual names (often in large letters) are frequently shown on armoured vehicles.

East Germany: olive drab or, sometimes, light grey. The national sign is in black, yellow, red and gold in a small circle.

West Germany: overall olive drab normally, but other disruptive colours are sometimes added e.g. brown or white (for winter snow). The national marking of a black Iron Cross with white outline is usually shown on armoured vehicles. Vehicle registration numbers, preceded by black, red and yellow rectangle and letter 'Y', are in black on a white rectangle or plate. Large white (or white outline) tactical numbers and/or small symbols denoting the type of unit are sometimes used. Frontier police (Bundesgrenze) have similar plates, but without a tricolour, and have the prefix 'BG'.

Hungary: olive drab. Military vehicle registrations are prefixed 'H', or series 'HA' to 'HZ', followed by a serial number in two groups of two figures. The registration serial is sometimes shown in large letters/numerals.

Irish Republic: overall olive drab. Military vehicle registration numbers are in the same overall series as civilian plates, although they are usually in the Dublin allocation.

Israel: overall yellow sand colour.

Italy: normally olive drab. The national sign (green, white and red rectangle) is carried at front and rear. Vehicle registration numbers are in black, prefixed by 'EI' and a green star, on a white plate for Army and Carabineri units.

Netherlands: overall olive drab. Vehicle registration numbers in black, prefixed by 'KL', 'KN' or 'KZ', on a yellow rectangle. A small rectangular national flag (red, white, and blue, horizontally divided) is shown at the front and rear of vehicles,

with the letters 'NL' (Nederland) in some cases. Unit and sub-unit badges and letters/figures are sometimes shown.

Poland: olive drab overall. The national sign, a red and white diamond, is carried on vehicles of armoured formations, which also often have large white three- or four-figure tactical numbers. Vehicle registration serials when shown are on the front, sides and rear, the latter sometimes in large letters/figures. Serials consist of two letters (the first being 'U' or 'D') followed by a four-figure number, all in white.

South Africa: khaki sand colour overall. Vehicle registration numbers are in white, with prefix 'R' (for Defence forces) on a black plate at the front and rear. Large white tactical numbers and letters (e.g. 72, 72A, 72B) are sometimes carried on the rear and sides of armoured vehicles.

U.S.S.R.: normally olive drab overall, although a second colour is sometimes added e.g. on Soviet Naval Infantry armoured personnel carriers. Large white three-figure tactical numbers (in some cases preceded by geometric shapes — circles or triangles) are often used on hull sides and rear. Red star or national badge markings are usually displayed on big parades but rarely in the field.

U.K.: normally olive drab or NATO green overall, with black disruptive patches added when required, or white, for winter snow conditions. Light stone and black is used in desert areas. Vehicle registrations consist of two numerals followed by two letters and two further numerals, usually stencilled straight on to the vehicle at the front and rear. Small white code figures (e.g. 103 or 4/2) carried at the front denote the unit and its place in its parent formation. Vehicles in B.A.O.R. (Germany) display a small painted Union flag at the front and rear. Many armoured units still use small diamond, triangle, square and circle signs to denote H.Q. and A, B, and C squadrons respectively.

U.S.A.: when a single colour (normally olive drab or forest green) is not used, a four-colour pattern is employed for tactical vehicles. This scheme consists of four colours selected from a standard range of 12. A typical combination is sand, (greyish, rather than yellow), earth red, dark green and black, the last two being used sparingly. This arrangement has been used by the U.S. Army in West Germany. The U.S. national sign used with the four-colour schemes is a black five-pointed star, and the U.S. Army vehicle registration serial (numerals, letter or letters and more numerals) is also in black.

Zimbabwe: armoured vehicles generally painted in a green and light brown disruptive camouflage pattern. Vehicle registrations consist of two numerals, two lettters and two numerals (and some vehicles have an additional terminal letter) all in white on a black rectangle. The two letters generally indicate the type of vehicle.

Belgium

Auto-blindée FN, Type G (Canon de 90-mm) and Auto-blindée FN, Type G (Mortier de 60-mm)

The Belgian Gendarmerie used American-built Staghound armoured cars and other wartime vehicles from 1945 until it was decided to replace them with armoured vehicles designed and built in Belgium. The Fabrique Nationale d'Armes de Guerre (FN) produced a prototype armoured car in July 1962 based on their FN4RM Ardennes series of one-ton trucks. A pilot model followed in September 1964 and was modified as the production pilot vehicle in July 1965. Production commenced in 1967 for the 90-mm gun model and the following year for the mortar-equipped version.

The FN armoured car, type G has an all-welded hull with the engine mounted at the rear. The four-speed gearbox transmits the power through a two-speed transfer box and thence to 'solid' axles at the front and rear. The suspension is of the semi-elliptic spring type with shock absorbers. Developing 130 h.p. at 3,500 r.p.m., the engine is a FN 652 petrol six-cylinder in-line model, giving the vehicle a maximum road speed of 110 km/h.

The driver occupies a central position behind the sloping front glacis plate, with three periscopes incorporated in his hatch. Optional direct vision is available through a bullet-proof window, normally covered by an armour plate visor. The other two crew members, the commander/loader (on the right) and the gunner, occupy the turret, located approximately in the centre of the vehicle. The commander has a dome-shaped cupola with an opening top and eight periscopes round its perimeter; the gunner has three periscopes and a flat hatch in the turret roof.

The mortar-armed version of the FN armoured car, in addition to the 60-mm mortar (for which 46 rounds are carried), has two coaxial 7.62-mm FN/MAG machine guns on the left side of the

Auto-blindée FN, Type G (Canon de 90-mm)

mounting. These have an elevation of up to 55 degrees, unlike the mortar which can be elevated to 75 degrees, and all these weapons have a depression of minus 10 degrees.

The cannon-armed version has a 90-mm Mecar gun, for which 40 rounds are carried, and one coaxial 7.62-mm FN/MAG machine gun. A pintle mounting, attached to the commander's cupola, for a further 7.62-mm machine gun is also provided on this version, although not normally on the mortar-equipped model. Both models have a total of 12 smoke grenades chargers, six mounted on each side of the turret.

A total of 62 FN type G armoured cars of both models were completed by 1971 and delivered to the Belgian Gendarmerie for use in the reconnaissance squadrons of the Mobile Groups.

Auto-blindée FN, Type G (Mortier de 60-mm)

Brazil

CTRA (EE-11 Urutu), CRR (EE-9 Cascavel), EE-17 Sucuri and EE-3 Jararaca

The rise of the Brazilian military vehicles industry has been remarkable. Following the production of military trucks of various kinds, the first armoured car known to be built in Brazil was completed in 1969 to designs by the Brazilian Army's Directorate of Research and Technical Education (D.P.E.T.).

The D.P.E.T. then collaborated with the automotive company Engesa-Engenheiros Especializados S.A. of Sao Paulo in designing, in early 1970, that company's first armoured vehicle, the six-wheeled armoured personnel carrier known to Engesa as EE-11 Urutu. The Urutu (named after a Brazilian poisonous snake) was followed almost immediately by the design and production of a prototype armoured reconnaissance car, the EE-9 Cascavel (rattlesnake) in late 1970. Development of improved versions of these two types was then followed by the appearance about the beginning of 1977 of a heavy armoured car known to Engesa as EE-17 Sucuri and, about a year later, by a scout car, the EE-3 Jararaca.

Apart from sales to the Brazilian forces, the EE-11 and EE-9 have been exported to several countries. Setting aside Brazil's freedom from some of the restraints imposed on many countries of the Western or Eastern blocs, the success of the Enegesa products can be put down to their simple robust design, their relative cheapness, and the manufacturer's willingness to provide variants to suit the particular needs of customer countries.

The EE-11 Urutu is a six-wheeled amphibious armoured personnel carrier, known to the Brazilian armed services as Carro de Transporte sobre Rodas Anfibio (C.T.R.A.). It has a fully water-proofed, fully enclosed, monocoque hull in which the engine is located on the front right-hand side, with the driver on the left, leaving an unob-

C.T.R.A. EE-11 Urutu (armoured personnel carrier)

C.T.R.A. EE-11 Urutu (armoured personnel carrier) swimming in the sea

structed rear compartment for 14 personnel. There are single doors on each side and in the rear plate and two long folding hatches in the roof of the rear compartment. The engine in the prototype and preproduction vehicles for the Brazilian army and marines is the Brazilian-manufactured Mercedes-Benz Model OM 352A six-cylinder in-line turbo-charged diesel producing 172 h.p. at 3,800 r.p.m.

The transmission in early vehicles consists of a manual five-speed gearbox with a two-speed transfer box. The front suspension is of the double wishbone type, controlled by coil springs with telescopic shock absorbers, while the rear wheels are carried on 'walking' beams on the rear axle which is sprung on longitudinal semi-elliptic leaf springs. This system permits up to 90 cm of vertical movement of the rear wheels.

The first batch of vehicles supplied to the marines (Urutu I) are capable of being operated in the open sea, water propulsion being by means of twin propellers, driven by shafts from the transfer box, at the rear of the hull. Steering is by three vanes (originally a single rudder) behind each

propeller tunnel. A trim vane is carried on the front glacis plate and a smooth-water speed of 12 km/h can be attained. Four (two on each side) plastic air-intake tubes are carried to provide air for the crew and engine when the vehicle is completely closed down in rough sea; this system enables the Urutu to operate in waves up to three metres high. The first batch of army vehicles (Urutu II) are not required to operate in rough sea, so they lack the propellers and breathing tubes and are propelled by their wheels in water. The Urutu III has amphibious equipment like Urutu I and a more powerful engine, the Detroit Diesel 6V53 developing 212 h.p., coupled with an Allison four-speed automatic transmission.

The normal armament of the Urutu armoured personnel carrier is a machine gun or light automatic gun (or combination of both) in a small turret, or alternatively a breech-loading mortar of the Hotchkiss-Brandt type. Specialised versions include an anti-aircraft vehicle, with the French TA 20 system and radar-controlled twin 20-mm Oerlikon cannon, and an armoured ambulance for four stretcher cases or six to eight sitting cases.

The Carro de Reconhecimento sobre Rodas (C.R.R.) (armoured reconnaissance car), as the EE-9 Cascavel is known to the Brazilian army, is a six-wheeled vehicle bearing a superficial resemblance to the U.S. M8 light armoured car of World War 2 with which the army was equipped. It has an automotive layout and suspension similar to that of the EE-11 Urutu, although the components are rearranged to provide the rear engine configuration typical of many armoured reconnaissance cars. In the preproduction batch of cars, the British Perkins 6357 engine made in Brazil was used, but the standard engine is the Brazilian-manufactured Mercedes Benz OM 352A. The hull is welded like that of the EE-11, but is much lower. The driver is at the front, slightly to the left of the centre line, with the turret, containing the other two crew members, immediately behind him. The turret was of cast construction in the prototype and was armed with a 37-mm gun and a 0.30-in machine gun, pending development of a 90-mm gun turret. The first vehicles delivered to the Brazilian army were, as an interim measure, fitted with 37-mm gun turrets removed from U.S. M3A1 light tanks.

The early vehicles were known as Cascavel I, but the first model with the 90-mm calibre weapon intended for the production series is Cascavel II, equipped with a French-built H-90 turret armed with the 90-mm DEFA D921A gun and a coaxial machine gun. The larger turret has necessitated widening and raising the height of the hull. Cascavel III has a turret similar in design to that of the second model, but is welded and mounts a gun designed by the Belgian company Cockerill. The gun, the smooth bore 90-mm EC-90/1–36 is also made in Brazil. The turret is made from the dual-hardness armour plate developed by Engesa and which comprises a hard outer layer bonded on to a softer but tougher inner layer. This steel was previously used only for the hulls of production-series Cascavels. A further improvement in the Cascavel III is the introduction of the Allison four-speed automatic transmission in place of the manual gearbox of earlier models. Finally, the Cascavel IV has a more powerful engine, the Detroit Diesel 6V53 of 212 h.p., an improved turret incorporating an externally mounted machine gun capable of being fired by the commander by remote control, and a

C.R.R. EE-9 Cascavel III (armoured car)

driver-controlled central tyre inflation system. This enables the driver to change tyre pressures quickly to suit the terrain.

The EE-17 Sucuri and EE-3 Jararaca complete the family of Engesa armoured vehicles, respectively at the top and bottom ends of the weight range. The Sucuri (not illustrated) is an 18.5-ton heavy armoured car intended for support. It has a French-designed oscillating turret, like that of the Dutch version of the AMX-13 tank, equipped with a 105-mm gun with semi-automatic loading and a coaxial machine gun. The engine is a six-cylinder Detroit Diesel 6V53T developing 300 h.p at 2,800 r.p.m and is mounted at the front next to the driver. The front suspension consists of semi-elliptical leaf springs with hydraulic shock absorbers, while the rear suspension is similar to that of the EE-11 and EE-9.

The scout or light reconnaissance car EE-3 Jararaca is a relatively simple four-wheel-drive vehicle using, for cheapness, many of the mechanical parts of the Engesa EE-15 1½-ton truck. The engine, mounted at the rear, is the Brazilian Mercedes Benz OM 314 four-cylinder water-cooled diesel. The manual gearbox has five speeds and is linked to a two-speed transfer box; the transmission is via 'solid' axles at front and rear. Semi-elliptic leaf spring suspension is used. The all-welded monocoque hull normally accommodates three, the driver at the front left side and the others in a central compartment behind. The armament can be a 12.7-mm heavy machine gun on an open ring mounting or a heavier weapon such as a 20-mm cannon, a 106-mm recoilless gun or missile launchers.

Sales of the EE-9 to Qatar, Libya and other countries have been reported, although the EE-11 (equipped with a British Scorpion turret) did not secure acceptance by Canada. Also, known as Hydracobra, several versions of the EE-11, including one with the 90-mm gun turret of the EE-9, are being offered for sale by the Bell Aerospace Division of Textron Inc. of Buffalo, N.Y., U.S.A.

EE-3 Jararaca (scout car)

Canada/Switzerland

Armoured Vehicles General Purpose

Mowag Motorwagen Fabrik A.G. of Kreuzlingen in Switzerland has developed various prototypes of wheeled armoured personnel carriers since the 1950s, including the Puma 6 × 6 vehicle in 1966 and the Piranha, in 8 × 8, 6 × 6 and 4 × 4 versions, from 1973 onwards. Piranha was among 14 different vehicles submitted by eight countries for evaluation by Canada as a general purpose armoured vehicle, and this Swiss vehicle in its 6 × 6 version was the one chosen for the Canadian army.

The requirement of the Canadian Land Forces was for a highly mobile armoured vehicle to equip both regular and militia units in Canada where few tanks are now based. These vehicles were needed for training in Canada itself and also to be available for rapid deployment in peace-keeping and internal security operations overseas, as well as for Canada's contribution to the NATO ACE Mobile Force. Hence, air-portability was an important consideration.

In the contract with Mowag, the Canadian government arranged that the Piranha should be built in Canada under licence using many components made in Canada, including the engine; that the hulls should be constructed of Canadian armour plate; and that Mowag would use Canadian-manufactured steel plate in armoured vehicles they produced themselves in Switzerland.

The Canadian version of Piranha is known as Armoured Vehicle General Purpose (A.V.G.P.) and comes in three models: Wheeled Armoured

Armoured Vehicle General Purpose–W.A.P.C. Grizzly

Armoured Vehicle General Purpose–W.F.S.V. Cougar

Personnel Carrier (W.A.P.C.) known as Grizzly; Wheeled Fire Support Vehicle (W.F.S.V.), or Cougar; and Wheeled Maintenance and Recovery Vehicle (W.M.R.V.), or Husky. The original order in 1977 for a total of 350 vehicles was subsequently extended to 261 Grizzlies, 189 Cougars and 26 Huskies.

The A.V.G.P.–W.A.P.C. Grizzly, which is closest to the Piranha 6 × 6 prototype, is a six-wheeled, six-wheel-drive vehicle with a crew of 11, having an all-welded steel hull constructed of armour plate supplied by Canadian Heat Treaters, Toronto. The driver is on the left side of the vehicle, with the engine on the right and the personnel compartment at the rear, access to which is through two large doors. There are two firing ports for small arms on each side of the hull and two more in the rear doors, thus making a total of six. On the roof of the rear compartment is a Cadillac Gage turret, mounting a 12.7-mm machine gun, a 7.62-mm machine gun and eight smoke grenade launchers (four on each side). The

engine is a 275-h.p. six-cylinder Detroit Diesel which gives a maximum road speed of 100 km/h. The Grizzly is amphibious, being driven in the water by two propellors located just behind and above the rear wheels. A trim plate is kept folded on the nose plate when not in use. The water speed is 10.5 km/h.

The A.V.G.P.–W.F.S.V. Cougar is identical both mechanically and in the general configuration of the hull, to the Grizzly and differs principally in the turret. This is like that of the British Scorpion Combat Vehicle Reconnaissance (Tracked) and is equipped with a 76-mm gun, a 7.62-mm coaxial machine gun and eight smoke grenade dischargers. The hull lacks the firing ports for the crew's personal weapons. Performance on land and water is almost identical to that of the Grizzly.

The A.V.G.P.–W.M.R.V. Husky is the same mechanically and in performance to both the Grizzly and the Cougar but is turretless and the rear part of the hull has a raised roof. In front of this and approximately in the centre of the vehicle is the turntable for the Hiab 650A hydraulic crane which has a 3.5-ton lifting capacity and when not in use is stowed over the rear of the vehicle. There is also a rear winch with an eight-ton pull. Fitter's equipment necessary for the maintainance and recovery of A.V.G.P.s in the field is carried in the Husky. For self-protection a 7.62-mm machine gun is carried on a pintle mounting attached to the vehicle commander's hatch just behind the driv-

er's position and there are eight smoke grenade dischargers mounted on the front of the raised part of the hull.

All three versions of the A.V.G.P. for the Canadian Land Forces were produced between 1978 and 1981 at a specially built plant of the Diesel Division of General Motors of Canada Ltd in London, Ontario.

Armoured Vehicle General Purpose–W.M.R.V. Husky

Czechoslovakia

PL dv K 30-mm (M53/59) Plate 1

This relatively simple vehicle, which entered service in 1959, was built for the Czechoslovak army as a mobile anti-aircraft weapon to combat low flying aircraft such as helicopter gunships. It consists of a six-wheeled (all-wheel-drive) Praga model V3S truck, with an armoured bonnet and cab, mounting twin model M53 30-mm automatic cannons on a fully rotating turntable. An armoured roofless compartment is provided for the gunner on the left side of the mounting. The commander is seated next to the driver and is provided with a transparent observation dome on the cab roof. The guns have a maximum rate of fire of up to 500 rounds per minute each, although the normal rate is 100 to 150 rounds per minute. They have an elevation of 90 degrees and a depression of minus 10 degrees, so that, with armour-piercing instead of high explosive rounds, they can also be used against light armoured vehicles. Their maximum range is about 8,000 metres, although effective range is only about a quarter of this distance.

The Praga truck which forms the automotive basis of this equipment is powered by a Tatra T912-2 air-cooled six-cylinder in-line diesel engine developing 110 h.p. at 2,200 r.p.m. It has a maximum road speed of 60 km/h and, although basically a commercial vehicle, it has a reasonably good cross-country performance because of its six-wheel drive.

Also supplied to Yugoslavia as well as the Czech army, the PL dv K 30-mm, although still effective against slow low-flying aircraft, is likely to be replaced by more sophisticated radar-controlled equipment capable of taking on all types of aircraft operating at low levels.

122-mm rocket launcher on Tatra 813 (M1972) Plates 2 and 3

Known to be employed by the East German army, this equipment is designated M1972 by NATO, from the year in which it is believed to have entered service. The Tatra 813 eight-wheeled heavy truck has been used as an armoured self-propelled mounting for the Soviet 40-tube launcher for BM21 122-mm rockets, together with an automatic 40-round reload system. The original Soviet mounting, which first appeared in 1964, was on an unarmoured six-wheeled lorry and did not have the reload system, so this Czech development is a considerable advance both in mobility, fire power and protection.

The BM21 rocket exists in two versions, one being 1.9 metres long, weighing 46 kg and having a maximum range of 14 km, and the other is

122-mm rocket launcher on Tatra 813 (M1972). This vehicle has a bulldozer blade fitted and the rocket launcher is in the elevated position

PLATE 1
PL dv K 30-mm (M53/59)
CZECHOSLOVAKIA

PLATE 2
**122-mm rocket launcher
on Tatra 813 (M1972)**
CZECHOSLOVAKIA

PLATE 3
**122-mm rocket launcher
on Tatra 813 (M1972)**
CZECHOSLOVAKIA

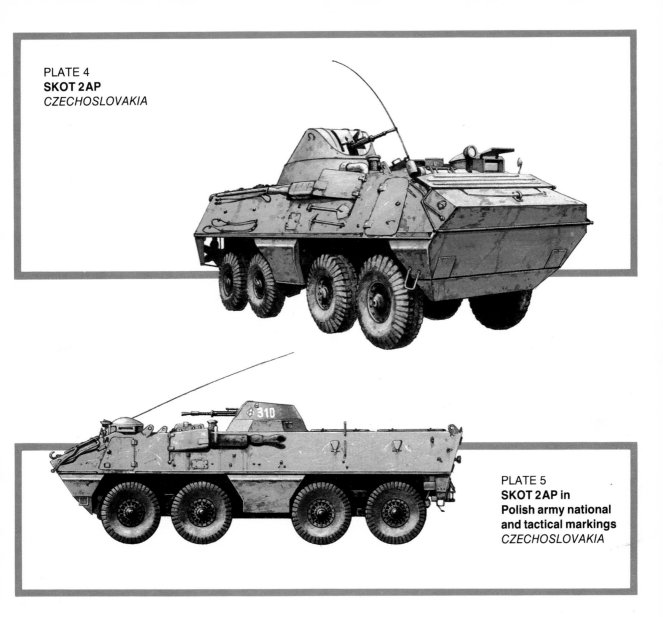

3.23 metres long, weighs 77 kg and has a range of 21 km. Single rounds can be fired from the launcher, as can salvos at a rate of three rounds per second. Automatic reloading of the tubes takes two minutes. The crew of four is carried in the armoured cab.

The eight-wheel-drive vehicle weighs 19 tons loaded and is powered by a Tatra T930 V-12 air-cooled diesel engine giving 270 h.p. at 2,700 r.p.m. The top road speed is 80 km/h and the maximum road range is 650 km. A dozer blade can be fitted at the front to help in preparing emplacements.

An armoured self-propelled 152-mm howitzer mounted on a rear-engined version of the Tatra 813 truck first appeared in public in Prague in 1980.

Obrneny Transporter OT-64 (SKOT)
Plates 4 and 5

Designed originally in Czechoslovakia to be a home-produced equivalent to the Soviet BTR-60, Poland joined the development programme at an early stage in 1961. Thereafter the two countries co-operated in the finalisation of the design which was known in Czechoslovakia as Středni Kolový Obrněny Transportér and by the Poles as Sredni

Kolowy Opancerzony Transporter (medium wheeled armoured transporter) or SKOT. Variants of the basic model were later constructed by each country to meet its special requirements.

One of the fundamental disadvantages of the Soviet BTR-60 as an armoured personnel carrier is its lack of rear access doors; personnel disembarked over the sides, being completely unprotected while doing so. In the OT-64/SKOT the engine is placed in a forward position, just behind the compartment for the operating crew (driver and vehicle commander). This enables all the rear part of the vehicle to be left free for the infantry personnel carried, who have two large doors in the back of the hull for entry and exit. The 18 infantrymen occupy longitudinal seats at either side and face inwards. Firing ports are provided in the hull sides and in the rear doors: additionally there are large hatches in the hull roof. The earliest Czech model of the OT-64 had no fixed armament, although the equivalent Polish version was fitted with a 7.62-mm machine gun on a pedestal mount; later, a curved shield was fitted and sometimes a 12.7-mm machine gun was used. This type was known as SKOT 2 by the Poles who were its only users.

The next model introduced the turret of the BTR-60PB (with 14.5-mm and 7.62-mm machine guns) mounted on the roof at the front of the personnel compartment on a 'collar' to enable the weapons to clear observation cupolas etc. on the hull roof. This version of the OT-64 was known as SKOT 2A. The addition of the turret reduced the number of the infantry carried from 18 to 15.

A further model, SKOT 2AP, was developed for the Polish army and had an enclosed turret that permitted the guns to be elevated to nearly 90 degrees for anti-aircraft use. Sagger anti-tank guided missiles have been added to the turret sides of some vehicles.

The engine of the OT-64 is the Tatra V-8 air-cooled diesel, developing 180 h.p. at 2,000 r.p.m., model T928-14 in early models and T928-18 for later vehicles. Both the engine and many of the automotive components are derived from the Tatra 813 8 × 8 heavy truck. The transmission is rather complicated: a transfer box at the front of the engine, which is situated roughly over the second pair of wheels, transmits the drive via differentials for the first and second pairs, and a second transfer box between the third and fourth pairs of wheels takes the drive similarly to these wheels. The suspension is independent on all wheels, the latter being carried on double wishbone arms with coil springs. For propulsion in water there is a power take-off to a small central transfer box and thence to propellers at either side. In water, a trim board, normally folded on the glacis plate, is erected. The vehicle has a maximum land speed of 95 km/h and in water can reach 9 km/h. At 14.5 tons the SKOT is heavier than the BTR-60PB and has a better performance but is less well protected, with a maximum of only 10 mm of armour.

Specialised versions of the OT-64/SKOT (all turretless) include the R2 and R3 command vehicles and the WPT-SKOT repair vehicle. Various versions have been exported to a number of African countries as well as Hungary, Syria and India.

Obrneny Transporter OT-64 (SKOT 2AP). This vehicle is in Polish service

Egypt

Walid Armoured Personnel Carrier
Plates 6 and 7

Although Egypt has modified imported tanks, the Walid wheeled armoured personnel carrier is the only type of armoured vehicle known to have been designed and built in Egypt. Apparently inspired by the Soviet BTR-40, numbers of which have been supplied to Egypt, the Walid is a four-wheel-drive vehicle powered by an air-cooled West German Deutz engine. This is probably the 5.32-litre air-cooled diesel of the Magirus-Deutz Mercur truck, produced under licence in Egypt and supplied in several versions to the Egyptian Army. It is likely that most of the automotive components are also derived from the Mercur truck.

With an all-welded hull, the engine and driver's cab is fully enclosed but the top of the crew compartment is open. A 7.62-mm machine gun can be mounted at the left-hand side of the roof of the driver's cab and operated from the crew compartment. There are also six firing ports in the hull, three on each side.

With a capacity for 10 troops, including the driver, the Walid, which appears to have been first produced in the mid-late 1960s, is probably now obsolescent in its original role. It has, however, more recently been adapted as a rocket carrier-launcher. The launcher for 12 rockets is mounted in the rear compartment and fires forwards over the cab. Walid armoured personnel carriers have been supplied to Algeria, the Yemen and the Palestine Liberation Organisation.

Walid armoured personnel carrier

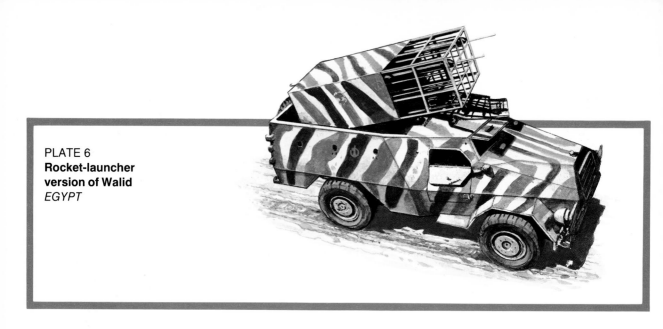

PLATE 6
**Rocket-launcher
version of Walid**
EGYPT

PLATE 7
Walid
EGYPT

France

Engin Blindé de Reconnaissance
Plates 8 and 9

In 1931 the French cavalry decided to classify their armoured fighting vehicles into three categories: Automitrailleuse de Découverte (AMD), Automitrailleuse de Reconnaissance (AMR), and Automitrailleuse de Combat (AMC). The latter were intended to take part in the main battle and were invariably tanks, although they were designated as 'armoured cars' because of the rivalry between the cavalry and the infantry who were officially responsible for combat tanks.

The AMD were responsible for long range reconnaissance, for which speed and a wide cir-

cuit of action were needed, and wheeled vehicles filled this category. The AMR were intended for close reconnaissance, and so only a limited fuel capacity was required, although the armour protection was of a somewhat higher standard. Wheeled, semi-tracked and full-tracked vehicles were all, at times, used in this category.

The specifications of the vehicles taken into service sometimes blurred the distinctions between the three classes of cavalry armoured fighting vehicles. This was particularly so between the AMD and AMR and, possibly for this reason, the cavalry command decided in 1937 to obtain a vehicle to combine the AMD and AMR categories. The specification for an Automitrailleuse puissante de Cavalerie was issued in 1938. This required, within a weight (not in fact attained) of seven tons, armament of one 37-mm gun and two machine guns, 40-mm armour, a

PLATE 8
EBR 75 Modèle 1951
FRANCE

PLATE 9
EBR-ETT
FRANCE

cross-country speed of 80 to 100 km/h, and the ability to cross a trench 1.3 metres wide. Designs for a six-wheeled and a half-tracked vehicle were produced by two manufacturers and Panhard designed an eight-wheeled *automitrailleuse puissante*. The prototype of the Panhard vehicle, Panhard Type 201, appeared in 1939 but development was arrested by the German invasion and subsequent occupation of France. The sole prototype of the Panhard Type 201 was evacuated to Morocco just before the armistice in 1940; it was lost during the War and the drawings were destroyed to prevent them being acquired by the enemy.

In March 1945, after France had been liberated but before the end of World War 2, the French army high command issued a specification for a wheeled Engin Blindé de Reconnaissance. The War had outmoded many pre-war theories, and the name as well as the specification reflected ideas for a new, mobile and very powerful armoured fighting vehicle weighing up to 12 tons and armed with a 75-mm gun, the calibre of the guns of most medium tanks still in use in 1945.

The firm of Panhard et Levassor, which as long ago as 1911 had supplied machine gun cars (unarmoured) for the French army, and whose Type 178 had been one of the best armoured cars of the early part of World War 2, again took part in a competition to provide the French army with an armoured car. Besides Panhard, three other experienced manufacturers were asked to produce designs for the EBR, and Lorraine came up with a six-wheeler, Latil with an eight-wheeler and Hotchkiss with another six-wheeler. The Lorraine design was rejected without even a prototype having been built. Latil built a prototype, as did Hotchkiss; the latter had six widely-spaced equidistant wheels and a turret mounted towards the rear. However, neither the Latil nor the Hotchkiss vehicles were proceeded with after 1950, by which time a Panhard had been selected as the EBR for the army.

Panhard produced designs for an eight-wheeled armoured car, known as Type 212, and a simplified version with only six wheels and torsion bar suspension. The prototype of the latter should have been ready in September 1948, but because of the success of the eight wheeler, which made its

debut in the preceding month, it seems never to have been completed.

The Panhard 212 drew heavily on the pre-war Type 201 design, of which, although it no longer existed in any tangible form, the main features were well known to the French design team; these features provided for an 8×8 vehicle with the central four wheels (steel rimmed and of the agricultural tractor type) capable of being raised for road work, drivers at each end, and a low centrally-mounted engine. The Type 201 had been, in fact, well ahead of its time and so many features of its mechanical layout could be used again after the War. The main difference in the post-war type was, of course, in the armament, which was mounted in an oscillating turret of new design. In this type of turret the whole top part is mounted on trunnions in the lower part. The gun, when elevated or depressed, does not move in relation to the turret, as in most A.F.V.s, but with the top half of the turret itself. This arrangement is easier to protect than a conventional gun mantlet and simplifies the installation of an automatic loading system.

The first production vehicle, the EBR 75 Modèle 1951, had a Type F.L.11 turret mounting a 75-mm gun of medium velocity, with a 7.5-mm (alternatively a 7.62-mm) coaxial machine gun. The Modèle 1954 was an improved version. Later vehicles (Modèle 54-10 and Modèle 55) had the F.L.10 turret (also used on the AMX-13 light tank) with a high velocity 75-mm gun coupled with an automatic loading system. Finally came the EBR 90, equipped with the 90-mm smooth-bore gun with fin-stabilised shaped-charge projectiles capable of penetrating 320 mm of steel armour, and hence able to destroy even main battle tanks. All models had the somewhat unusual feature of fixed machine guns in the nose plate and corresponding rear plate, being fired by the front and rear drivers. These guns were often omitted in service, however.

The power unit of the EBR was specially developed for it, and is a remarkably low 12-cylinder horizontally-opposed air-cooled engine. Although almost directly under the turret ring, the hull height has been kept to only just over one metre, and the EBR's overall height is only 2.24 metres. The engine produces 200 h.p. at

3,700 r.p.m. and gives the vehicle a maximum speed of 100 km/h. The transmission is complicated, to gain the maximum advantage in reducing height. In front of the engine is the clutch, then a four-speed gearbox, from which the drive is transmitted to a second gearbox, transversely mounted, which, combined with the first, gives an option of 16 speeds, forward or reverse. From differentials either side of the second gearbox two drive shafts are carried forward to the front wheels, which are mounted on leading arms and sprung with coil springs and telescopic shock absorbers. The transmission for the two centre pairs of wheels (on leading and trailing arms, respectively) and the rear pair (on trailing arms) is carried back from the two differentials via shafts which follow the inside edges of the hull. The suspension of the rear pair of wheels is similar, although on trailing arms, to that of the front pair; all four wheels are steerable, although normally only the pair that are leading are used for this purpose when the centre four wheels are raised. With eight wheels in contact with the ground, four-wheel steering is automatically engaged. The four tractor-type wheels are sprung hydro-pneumatically by a system which is also used to raise or lower them. The front and rear wheels have tyres with gas-filled cells to enable them to continue to support the vehicle when they are punctured.

The hull of the EBR is a regular elongated octagon in plan, tapering to a small 'nose' plate at the front and rear. The armour thickness varies from 40 to 16 mm. With a driver at each end, the 'front' of the vehicle can normally only be distinguished by the rear-view mirrors and, in later models, by the air vents on the top edge of the hull over the rear pair of tractor-type wheels. In addition to the drivers, the other crew members are the commander (on the left) and the gunner who occupy seats mounted in the upper part of the oscillating turret.

An experimental version of the EBR had an anti-aircraft turret mounting two Hispano-Suiza Type 831 30-mm automatic cannon. There was also an experimental turretless command version. A canvas screen, like those of British wartime D.D. tanks, was tested to make the EBR amphibious but was not satisfactory.

The Panhard Type 238 was an armoured personnel carrier known as EBR-ETT. This used most of the mechanical components of the EBR 75 but had only one driving position and a raised hull capable of carrying, in addition to the driver, 14 personnel for whom access was via two large doors at the rear. The prototype had a small turret at the front of the hull roof, mounting one machine gun; later vehicles, apparently, had two command cupolas instead. Only a small number of vehicles was built for the French army, although some (possibly from the same batch) were eventually acquired by Portugal.

Some 1,200 EBR 75s and EBR 90s were built, most of which were supplied to the French army. Although they have been largely superseded by more modern vehicles in the country of their origin, they remain in service in some of the countries to which they were exported, including Portugal. Despite its long and interesting history the EBR 75/90 still remains a quite formidable vehicle.

Automitrailleuse Légère AML HE 60-7 and Automitrailleuse Légère AML H-90
Plates 10 and 11

The French army operations in Algeria in the 1950s showed the need for an armoured car much lighter and easier to maintain in the field than the eight-wheeled EBR. Some Ferret Mk 1 and Mk 2 scout cars were purchased from Britain as an immediate measure and it was at first proposed to produce the Ferret under licence in France. However, there was strong resistance by French industry to this proposal and the Ferret's armament, a single machine gun, was considered to be inadequate for the requirements of the French army. Accordingly, a specification was drawn up by the beginning of 1956 for an armoured car which was air-transportable (having a loaded weight of 4.2 tons), capable of operating in the tropics, had a range of 500 km, a speed of 80/90 km/h, and a crew of three, two of which, if possible, were to be accommodated in a turret mounting two machine guns and a mortar.

Designs were produced by Saviem (supported by Renault and Simca) and Panhard — the latter's at first had only a one-man turret. Following

PLATE 10
**AML H-90 of the
French army**
FRANCE

PLATE 11
**AML HE 60-7 of
the French Gendarmerie**
FRANCE

full-size wooden models, mild steel prototypes were built, the first Saviem vehicle being completed in 1957, but because modifications were needed, the Panhard AML was not ready until April 1959. In the meantime, the government agency DEFA (Direction des Études et Fabrications d'Armement), in conjunction with AMX (Atelier d'Issy-les-Moulineaux), designed a vehicle using some components of the British Ferret and a turret produced by AHE (L'Atelier du Havre) in order to further the development of the AML project. This prototype, AML SL 420, emerged from the workshops at the same time as the first Panhard prototype, AML 242.

The Saviem model had been dropped by this time and it was eventually decided to concentrate all effort on the development of the Panhard AML. The development of the DEFA/AMX AML was ceased but its turret (built by AHE), which was of a satisfactory design, was made available for the Panhard. The later Panhard production prototypes had their turret rings redesigned to take the AHE turrets. With larger diameter tyres and other lesser modifications, these became the AML 245, the production model.

During 1959 consideration had been given by the army to its detailed requirements for light armoured vehicles of the AML series, and three basic types were finally ordered: the original version with a 60-mm mortar and two 7.5-mm (later 7.62-mm) machine guns, but with a variant having one heavy 12.7-mm machine gun instead of the two light machine guns; a version with a 90-mm cannon and one 7.5-mm coaxial machine gun (and another mounted on the turret roof, a requirement that was later dropped; and a troop-carrying version.

A rearrangement of the automotive components and a fully redesigned hull were required for the troop carrier, described separately here. The two mortar and machine gun versions were ready for production and the first of these reached the army in 1961. They were designated AML HE 60-7 (two machine guns) and AML HE 60-12. A

design for a 90-mm gun turret was in existence in 1959, when a wooden model was demonstrated on the AML by DEFA/AMX, and a steel prototype was completed in 1960 which finally went into production in early 1964. This type is known officially as AML H-90 Mle Fl.

The AML 245, to give it its manufacturers designation, is a four-wheeled, four-wheel-drive vehicle with an all-welded hull in which the engine is located at the rear. The engine is a Panhard model 4 HD horizontally-opposed four-cylinder air-cooled petrol type developing 90 h.p. at 4,700 r.p.m. The gearbox (with six forward and one reverse gears) with a central differential is in front of the engine. Power is transmitted via two cross-shafts to transfer boxes with differentials at either side, distributing the power between front and rear wheels on each side. From here the power is taken the short distance to the rear wheels through shafts and gears in the trailing arms of the suspension. The power to the front wheels is taken via universally-jointed shafts on each side, inside the outer edge of the hull, which is best described as an elongated seven-sided structure in plan, widening out in the middle.

Automitrailleuse Légère AML H-90

The front wheels are also on trailing arms and the final drive is similar to that at the rear. The trailing arms of the suspension are controlled by a single coil spring with a concentric telescopic shock absorber at each wheel station. The tyres are Michelin 11.00 × 16-XL, with inner tubes containing a large number of small cells permanently inflated with gas which partly fill the tyres. The vehicle can continue to run supported by these tubes when the tyres have been punctured.

The driver of the AML is in the centre of the hull at the front and the commander and gunner are behind him in the turret. Apart from the hatches in the turret roof, access is by means of doors on both sides of the hull just behind the front wheels. The underside of the hull is V-shaped, helping to deflect mine-blast.

The turret of the AML HE 60-7 and HE 60-12 is a low circular structure with the 60-mm mortar mounted to the right of centre and the two machine guns (or single 12.7-mm machine gun in the HE 60-12) to the left. The original twin machine guns were 7.5-mm in calibre but the NATO 7.62-mm calibre have since become standard. The 60-mm breech-loaded mortar can be used for direct or indirect fire, with ranges of up to about 300 metres and 1,700 metres respectively. There are two types of mortar, the Hotchkiss-Brandt CM 60 A1 and the DTDT Model CS. The latter type is fitted in vehicles supplied to the French Gendarmerie, which also use the AML.

The AML H-90 has a much larger turret than the HE 60 series. It is welded and has considerable overhang at the rear. The 90-mm gun is mounted centrally with the coaxial machine gun on the left. A smooth bore weapon, the 90-mm fires fin-stabilised projectiles, both shaped-charge armour piercing (H.E.A.T.) and high explosive. The effective range is up to 2,000 metres for H.E.A.T. and 1,500 metres for H.E.

Different versions of the Panhard AML 245 have been sold to around 30 different countries and they have also been produced in considerable numbers under licence in South Africa where they are known as Eland.

Véhicule de Transport de Troupe, M.3 (Panhard) Plates 12 and 13

Derived from the AML series of light armoured cars, with which it shares some 95 per cent of its mechanical components, the M.3 armoured personnel carrier was originally expected to be the third in the family of Panhard light armoured vehicles to be used by the French army. Although a modified version, the Panhard M.4, was produced for the armoured personnel carrier trials, the Saviem VAB was chosen instead for this role. Nevertheless, the Panhard M.3 has had considerable success abroad, its different versions having been bought by about a dozen countries, most of which also use vehicles of the AML 245 series.

The prototype of the M.3 appeared in June 1969 and a version with an improved hull shape, which became the production model, had satisfactorily completed trials by the end of 1970. Although, as mentioned, the majority of the automotive components of the AML 245 have been used in the M.3, the desirability of a clear compartment at the rear with access doors in the back of the hull led to the rearrangement of the engine near the front just behind the driver. Both the wheelbase and track have been increased, compared with the AML 245, so that the roomy hull can carry 12 troops (including the driver) and the vehicle (unlike the AML 245) is amphibious without special preparation. This is facilitated by the location of the air inlets and outlets of the engine cooling system and the exhaust on the roof of the hull. Propulsion in water is by means of the road wheels and the maximum speed is four km/h. There is exceptionally good provision for rapid deployment of the infantrymen carried, with a door each side of the hull and two doors in the rear plate. Six large firing ports are provided in the hull sides and one in each rear door. In the basic version there were two hatches, in the hull roof, from which machine guns or other light weapons could be operated. The personnel carrier role includes towing the 120-mm infantry mortar and transporting its crew.

The M.3 has been produced in a variety of versions, both as personnel carrier and supporting vehicle. As an alternative to the optional hull-roof mountings, various combinations of 7.62-mm and 12.7-mm machine guns, 20-mm cannon and rocket launchers with or without turrets have been offered. Other armaments are the 81-mm VPM breech-loading mortar in a turret; the 60-mm Hotchkiss-Brandt CM 60A1 breech- or muzzle-loading mortar in an open mounting; a quadruple mounting of the HOT anti-tank missile; and twin Oerlikon 20-mm cannon in an anti-aircraft turret with associated radar.

Versions without fixed armament are a four-stretcher ambulance with a crew of three; a workshop vehicle carrying lifting tackle, genera-tor, welding equipment, bench, vice, tools, and a crew of five; a command vehicle with map tables etc. for the commander and his staff in the front crew compartment and radio equipment with two operators at the rear; and a cargo carrier with a capacity of 1,350 kg.

Véhicule de Transport de Troupe, M.3 (Panhard)

Engin de Reconnaissance Canon, ERC-90S, Sagaie and Engin de Reconnaissance Canon, ERC-90, Lynx
Plates 14 and 15

The Société de Constructions Mécaniques Panhard et Levassor has produced a successor to the AML 245 that has both a better cross-country perfor-mance and a very powerful gun but weighs less than 7,500 kg. Developed between 1975 and 1977, when the Engin de Reconnaissance Canon, or ERC-90S, was shown at the Satory exhibition of French army weapons and equipment, this vehi-cle benefited from the experience gained by Panhard with the experimental armoured vehicles M.2, M.4, M.6 and M.8, as well as the mass-produced AML and M.3. While avoiding features such as a hydro-pneumatic suspension system that enabled ground clearance to be changed (and tried out in some of the experimental vehicles). Panhard have concentrated on producing an effec-

tive fighting vehicle having the essentials in performance required in the 1980s.

A six-wheeled, six-wheel-drive vehicle, the ERC-90S Sagaie (assegai, an African spear) has the facility for raising the centre pair of wheels for operation on roads. These wheels remain driven when raised to avoid unnecessary complications in the transmission. Also, they are not steerable, only the two front wheels being used for steer-

ing. This wheel system permits fast economic operation on roads on four wheels (the maximum speed being 110 km/h) as well as providing the maximum traction and bearing surface when travelling cross-country. The basic version of the ERC-90S is not amphibious, although it can ford streams up to 1.2 metres deep. It can be made amphibious, however, by the addition of foam-filled sheet metal buoyancy chambers at the sides

PLATE 12
VTT-M.3, with twin-machine gun mounting, belonging to Irish Republic
FRANCE

PLATE 13
VTT-M.3 with open M.G. mounting
FRANCE

over the centre and rear wheels. A see-through trimboard is erected on the front of the glacis plate and the vehicle is propelled either by its wheels or by added Dowty-Messier twin hydrojets. These are located above and behind the rear wheels, and the exit ducts can be swivelled to steer the vehicle in water, where a maximum speed of nine km/h can be attained, roughly double that possible when propelled by the road wheels.

The all-welded steel hull of the ERC-90S has a configuration not unlike that of its smaller prede-

cessor the AML 245 in plan, widening out from the nose to the fighting compartment in the centre, with a 1.7-metre-diameter turret ring, and the narrower, parallel-sided engine compartment at the rear. The underside forms a shallow V to help deflect mine blasts and improve the vehicle's ability to cross soft ground. The driver sits over the centre line of the vehicle and behind him the commander in the left-hand side of the turret and the gunner at the right. The engine is a Peugeot V-6 spark-ignition type, modified from one used in passenger cars of that make. It develops

PLATE 14
ERC-90 Lynx
FRANCE

PLATE 15
ERC-90S (Sagaie)
with trim-board raised
FRANCE

140 h.p. at 5,250 r.p.m. and is water-cooled. An interesting feature is that cooling is by direct water-to-water heat transfer when the vehicle is operating in water, the radiator compartment, which is sealed from the engine compartment, being flooded and the radiator cooling fan disengaged.

The ERC's transmission is taken forward from the engine, via a tranversely-mounted gearbox with six forward speeds and reverse, by shafts at either side to the centre pair of wheels. From here further shafts take the power on to the front wheels. The rear pair of wheels are driven by shafts running back from the gearbox. The suspension of the front and rear wheels is on trailing arms controlled by a single coil spring at each wheel with an hydraulic shock absorber. The centre pair of wheels have a different hydropneumatic suspension system which can also be used to raise the wheels for road operation.

The ERC-90S is equipped with a long barreled 90-mm smooth-bore gun, firing fin-stabilised projectiles capable of penetrating up to 320 mm of steel armour, and a coaxially mounted 7.62-mm machine gun. The penetrative power of the gun gives it the capability of taking on even medium tanks, but another version of the ERC has a

lower-powered 90-mm gun, similar to that of the AML H-90, which is adequate for most reconnaissance missions. This version, the ERC-90 Lynx, has the advantage of being nearly 500 kg lighter than the Sagaie with some slight improvement in performance, although mechanically it is the same. Another armament alternative is the Hotchkiss-Brandt 81-mm muzzle or breech loading mortar. This can fire fin-stabilised armour-piercing projectiles as well as the usual high explosive mortar bombs. The fire support vehicle with this armament is known as Engin Mortier-Canon EMC-81. Also available is the ERC TG-120 Guépard (cheetah) which has a 20-mm automatic cannon and a 7.62-mm machine gun.

Véhicule de Combat à Roues, VCR
Plates 16 and 17

In a parallel development to the ERC, corresponding to that earlier for the AML and M.3, Panhard have produced an armoured personnel carrier (Transport de Troupe, or TT) and allied vehicles.

The engine in the Véhicule de Combat à Roues (VCR) series is identical to that of the ERC and is located just behind the driver on the right-hand

Engin de Reconnaissance Canon, ERC-90 Lynx

side of the hull. Although the gearbox is situated behind the engine in the VCR, instead of at the front, the transmission arrangement is otherwise the same in both ERC and VCR. With the transmission shafts running inside the hull at the sides, instead of down the centre as in some vehicles, an unobstructed floor is provided for the crew compartment at the rear and also allows the overall height to be kept down.

The standard personnel-carrying version, the VCR-TT, can accommodate 12 troops including the driver and the vehicle commander. Built out from the left-hand side of the driver's compartment and slightly raised above it is a multi-sided cupola for the commander on which a machine gun can be mounted. Behind this is the personnel compartment for 10 troops sitting on longitudinal seats. Three firing ports are provided on each side of the hull in addition to a hatch in the roof near the rear over which a 7.62-mm machine gun can be mounted. The six-wheeled arrangement precludes the provision of side doors as in the Panhard M.3, but there is a single large door at the rear which, unusually, does not have a firing port. The armament of the VCR-TT can be enhanced with a turret, in the centre of the vehicle behind the driver, for a 20-mm cannon and 7.62-mm machine gun, although this reduces by three the number of personnel that can be carried. Alternatively, a UTM 800 turret can be mounted in this position. This type of turret has quadruple HOT anti-tank guided missile launchers. In addition to the four missiles carried in the launcher, 10 reserve missiles are stored in the hull and these can be loaded by the crew under cover by means of an electrically-powered hoist. The HOT shaped-charge warheads can penetrate 800 mm of steel armour and have a maximum range of 4,000 metres. The vehicle in this version has a crew of four and is known as VCR-TH (Tourelle HOT).

An unarmed version of the VCR is VCR-IS (Intervention Sanitaire). This armoured ambulance is in most respects like the standard VCR-TT, but the roof of the rear compartment is raised to allow the medical personnel to work standing up if necessary. Four stretcher cases can be carried, or two stretcher cases and six seated patients, as well as two medical staff and the driver.

Véhicule de Combat à Roues–VCR. This version has a 20-mm cannon and the centre pair of wheels are shown raised for travel on roads

PLATE 16
VCR with HOT mounting
FRANCE

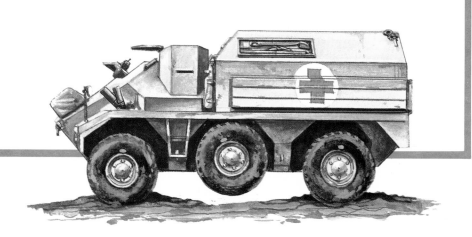

PLATE 17
**VCR-IS (ambulance)
with centre pair
of wheels raised**
FRANCE

Véhicule de l'Avant Blindé, VAB (Renault) (4 × 4) Plates 18 and 19

One result of the French army's invitation in 1969 for designs for a multipurpose light wheeled armoured vehicle is several broadly similar vehicles available for export. The vehicle that was successful in the trials for the French army contract was, however, the one submitted by Saviem, part of the Renault group.

Known as Véhicule de l'Avant Blindé (Advanced-Front (or Forward Area) Armoured Vehicle) or VAB, it has been produced in two main basic forms, 4 × 4 and 6 × 6, both having a hull of the same overall configuration and dimensions. The 4 × 4 version was adopted by the French army in 1974 and went into series production so that the first infantry regiment was fully equipped by 1978. Initial orders were for some 1,800 vehicles, but it is estimated that the French army may eventually require a total of up to 5,000 of both basic types. The VAB has been exported to at least three African and Asian countries and is said to be on order for several others.

The specification called for good mobility on and off the road, N.B.C. protection, adequate protection against light weapons and shell splinters, amphibious capability without preparation,

adaptability to a wide variety of roles, and relative ease of maintenance and operation. Above all a vehicle capable of being readily mass-produced, and therefore without excessive complication, was required. The Saviem solution was to design a vehicle using standard commercial components as far as possible with a straight-forward layout of transmission and suspension systems.

The engine of the VAB is a Saviem-built MAN (German design) type D.2356 HM72 six-cylinder diesel developing 220 h.p. at 2,200 r.p.m. It is

PLATE 18
VAB-VTT (4 × 4)
FRANCE

PLATE 19
VDAA (VCS TA20)
FRANCE

mounted on the centre line of the vehicle behind the driver and commander. The gearbox, which is either a five-speed Saviem Transfluid type with torque converter or a six-speed manual model, is in front of the engine with a differential under the nose plate. The transmission is led back via universal joints and differentials to the front wheels and thence to the rear wheels. The suspension is independent on all four wheels and consists of twin longitudinal torsion bars on each wheel with hydraulic shock absorbers. The tyres have a limited deflation device, being only partly air-filled. The greater part of the internal space is occupied by a large number of small cells that can support the vehicle if the tyres are pierced.

For operation in water, for which no special preparation is needed apart from the erection of a trim board, two hydrojets driven from a power take-off from the engine via the rear differential are used. The hydrojets, which have variable thrust for steering, are mounted just behind the rear wheels. This equipment is a relatively simple addition to the basic vehicle and only a small proportion of the French army's VABs in fact have it.

The two crew compartments of the welded hull of the VAB are divided laterally by the engine in an insulated compartment. A narrow corridor on the right-hand side allows communication between the driver and commander at the front and the compartment at the rear, which can carry up to 10 soldiers. There are three firing ports in each side of the hull and one in each side of the two doors at the rear. In the roof there are two hatches over the front compartment and two near the rear, with another in the centre just behind the engine. A 7.62-mm machine gun can be mounted in place of the commander's hatch, either behind a shield or in a small turret. An alternative is a 12.7-mm heavy machine gun mounted over the central hatch. By reducing the number of personnel in the rear compartment heavier armament can be carried, for example a 20-mm cannon or a turret with a 60-mm mortar and two machine guns, and quadruple mountings for the Mephisto or HOT anti-tank missile launchers have been demonstrated on 4 × 4 VABs. Command, radio, ambulance, cargo and internal security versions are also available.

The 4 × 4 VAB chassis has also been used for

Véhicule de l'Avant Blindé, VAB (4 × 4) with quadruple mounting for the Mephisto anti-tank missile launcher

two experimental anti-aircraft systems for the defence of armoured units, one of which should eventually be adopted by the French Army. One model, known as VADAR, has a GIAT GTS2 turret mounted near the rear of the hull roof. This two-man turret has two 20-mm F2 cannon and a Rodeo surveillance radar. The other model incorporates the Sociéte Electronique Marcel Dassault TA20 weapons system. This consists of a one-man turret, mounted near the hull centre, in which two 20-mm HSS820SL cannon are controlled by an E.M.D. surveillance radar. This type, unlike VADAR, has a modified hull with a smaller driver's cab. It is known as VDAA (Véhicule d'Auto-Défense Anti-Aérienne), or VCS TA20, and is shown here as a typical adaptation of the basic VAB chassis.

The name Saviem appears on many prototypes of the VAB and on early production vehicles, but since Saviem was combined with Automobiles M. Berliet to form Renault Véhicules Industriels, the Renault designation is now used.

Véhicule de l'Avant Blindé, VAB (Renault) (6 × 6) Plates 20 and 21

The Saviem (now Renault) VAB was produced in two forms, the second of which, the six-wheeled version, was not initially adopted by the French army. It shares nearly all the features of its design, including an almost identical hull, with the 4 × 4 version and uses only a slightly more complicated drive train (an extra differential has been inserted). The wheel base remains unaltered, the middle pair of wheels (which are steerable) having been added equidistant from the front and rear pairs. Performance figures, such as the maximum road speed of 92 km/h and water speed of 7 km/h are claimed to be identical, although the 6 × 6 vehicle is 1,000 kg heavier and has a better cross-country and ditch-crossing ability.

Provision has been made in the design of both the four-wheeled and the six-wheeled versions of VAB for the engine to be located at the rear. This arrangement is suitable for versions not used for personnel or cargo carrying and, in practice, is more likely to be used in the 6 × 6 vehicle which provides a better platform for heavier weapons such as the TG 120 turret mounting a 20-mm cannon and one machine gun, a twin 20-mm anti-aircraft turret, or a turret mounting a 90-mm gun and one or two machine guns. A new model with a modified hull, VBC 90, is under development. Another use for the 6 × 6 VAB (front-engined version) is as a tractor for the 120-mm Hotchkiss-Brandt rifled mortar and its crew. Alternatively the smaller CB mortar can be carried in, and fired from, the rear compartment.

Véhicule de l'Avant Blindé, VAB (6 × 6). This version has a 7.62-mm machine-gun turret

PLATE 20
VAB-VTT (6 × 6)
FRANCE

PLATE 21
VAB-VTT (6 × 6)
with TG 120 mounting with
one 20-mm gun and M.G.
FRANCE

Systeme d'Armes Missile Sol-air
'Crotale' TH.D 5000 Plates 22 and 23

The Crotale is a short range anti-aircraft missile system that is both highly mobile and air-portable. The system is carried in two vehicles, the acquisition unit and the firing unit, although one acquisition unit can control up to three firing units. The two types of vehicle, which are only very lightly armoured (up to five mm) are closely similar in their automotive characteristics and general layout. Electric power propels the vehicles as well as providing their own electric systems and air conditioning. An electric motor with associ-

ated epicyclic reduction gears drives each wheel; the four electric motors are supplied by an alternator driven by a thermal motor. A maximum of 70 km/h on the road can be attained. The suspension system is pneumatic and the height of the vehicle can be adjusted for different ground conditions. There are also three hydraulic stabilising jacks which are lowered when the vehicle is stopped and the anti-aircraft system is in operation.

The driver sits at the front in the centre and the

PLATE 22
**Crotale firing vehicle
in French Armée
de l'Air markings**
FRANCE

PLATE 23
**Crotale acquisition
vehicle in French Armée
de l'Air markings**
FRANCE

other two crew members occupy the cabin behind containing the controls for either the acquisition system or the missiles. The acquisition vehicle is distinguished externally by the oval dish of its radar on a revolving mounting, and the firing vehicle by the four missiles in their launcher-containers on either side of the bowl of their guidance radar.

In action, an aircraft is picked up by the acquisition vehicle's surveillance radar, which has an effective range of 18 km, and identified by an automatic target evaluation system. An interrogator unit decides if the aircraft is friendly or an enemy. A real-time digital computer analyses the data and if the aircraft is an enemy and is adjudged to be an immediate threat, an emergency programme brings into operation the interception calculations, which in less urgent circumstances are handled by the human controller. The computer-produced calculations are transmitted to the firing unit .by cable for distances up to 400 metres only, or by radio transmitter for any distance from 50 to 5,000 metres.

When a decision has been made to intercept the target, the firing vehicle's radar is directed on to it from the computer data received, and target interception course data is then fed through to the guidance system of the missile or missiles to be fired. In flight, immediately after firing, the missile is guided by an infra-red rangefinder acting on the missile's own propellant flame until its remote control device is fed with data from its tracking radar to correct its course. The missile is controlled in flight by aerodynamic means (rather than by varying the direction of the jet thrust as in some systems) with sustained advantages over its whole flight. Near the target, the infra-red target proximity device guides the missile to the final explosion of the 15 kg warhead. A maximum of six seconds is taken from detecting the target to launching the missile, which has an effective range of between 500 and 8,500 metres and a maximum altitude of 3,000 metres.

The Crotale system was developed from 1964 onwards, Thomson-CSF being responsible for the radar and electronics, Engins Matra for the missile, and the vehicles were built by Hotchkiss-Brandt (and, later, Creusot-Loire). Development was completed by 1969 and the first production units were delivered to the French Armée de l'Air (to be used for key airfield defence) and the South African government in 1972. South Africa, in fact, paid a high proportion of the cost of the whole project, which is known there as Cactus. Other countries using Crotale are Egypt, Kuwait, Libya, Pakistan and Spain.

Berliet VXB-170 Plates 24 and 25

The French lorry-building firm of Automobiles M. Berliet, suppliers of load carrying vehicles

for the French army, designed and produced as a private venture a prototype multipurpose armoured vehicle which appeared in 1968. This vehicle, known as BL-12 could carry 12 soldiers and was powered by a standard 160 h.p. Berliet diesel engine. After the BL-12 had been tested by the French army, an improved model, known as VXB-170 was completed by 1971. This was entered in the French army's trials for a Véhicule de l'Avant Blindé (VAB) against Panhard and Saviem competition. Because, by then, army opinion had decided on the need for full-size rear doors in a vehicle that would have personnel carrying as one of its main roles, the VXB with its rear-mounted engine was eliminated from the competition, which was won by the Saviem design. Independent evaluation was, however, carried out by the French Gendarmerie Nationale, which decided that the VXB-170 was the vehicle best suited to the requirements of its Défense Opérationelle du Territoire mobile units and placed an order with Berliet for 50.

The VXB-170 was produced in two broad categories, combat and internal security, with many variants available in each category. However, all use the same basic type of hull, an all-welded structure, and the automotive characteristics are shared by all versions. The engine is a Berliet V-8 diesel developing 170 h.p. at 3,000 r.p.m. This is located at the rear of the vehicle on the left-hand side, permitting access to the main compartment via a single rear door and a corridor on the right-hand side. The transmission is taken forward to a transfer box roughly in the centre of the vehicle and thence to differentials on the front and rear axles. The gearbox has six forward speeds with either a preselective or a manual control. Double concentric helical springs with hydraulic shock absorbers form the suspension, and the tyres are of the puncture-proof inner tube type, filled largely with small cells.

The main difference between the internal security type of VXB-170 as used by the French Gendarmerie and the various combat versions is that the former has a bullet-proof windscreen and lateral vision ports reinforced by close mesh wire grilles. Also, although available on all models, the optional hydraulically operated bulldozer blade is mainly intended for the Gendarmerie's use in clearing street obstacles. An hydraulic hoist with 3,500 to 4,500 kg capacity is another optional extra for special occasions. As a personnel carrier, there is accommodation for up to 15 including the driver, although 12 is the normal number carried. Two command vehicle variants are for section and platoon commanders respectively: the first carrying six personnel with three radio sets, a broadcasting system with loudspeakers, and a map table; the second carrying 12 personnel with two radio sets. The normal armament for the Gendarmerie versions is one machine gun on a ring mounting in the hull roof just behind the driver's cab.

Three African countries have purchased the VXB-170 in, it is assumed, its combat configuration, which is available in three main versions: VTT (Véhicule de Transport de Troupe, or personnel carrier), VRL (Véhicule de Reconnaissance Léger, or light reconnaissance vehicle) and VLC (Véhicule Léger de Combat, or light combat vehicle). All these have armoured visors to cover the bullet-proof glass windows for the driver and gun ports. In addition, three fixed episcopes are provided for the driver, and one rotating one for the commander, for use when closed down in action.

The main armament in all three main versions

Military armoured personnel carrier version of Berliet VXB-170

PLATE 24
**VXB-170 fitted with
dozer used by
French Gendarmerie**
FRANCE

PLATE 25
VXB-170
FRANCE

is mounted on the hull roof near the front, and in the VXB-170 VTT can be either a single 7.62-mm or 12.7-mm machine gun on an open mounting or twin 7.62-mm machine guns in a small turret. Twelve troops are normally carried, although 2,000-kg cargo-carrying, command and ambulance variants are available. The VRL has a turret mounting a 20-mm cannon and 7.62-mm machine gun and the VLC can have either a turret with a 60-mm mortar and a 12.7-mm machine gun or two 7.62-mm machine guns, a turret with a 20-mm cannon and two machine guns (12.7-mm and 7.62-mm), or a 90-mm smooth-bore gun turret with a coaxial 7.62-mm machine gun.

A simpler and cheaper vehicle than many of its competitors, the VXB-170 has a satisfactory cross-country performance and a maximum road speed of 85 km/h. It is also amphibious without special preparation and can achieve five km/h in water propelled by its wheels.

AMX-10RC Plate 26

More closely approaching a tank in many of its characteristics than most wheeled armoured vehicles today, the AMX-10RC features both skid-steering and a turret armament comparable with that of many medium tanks. Following trials with an experimental tracked vehicle, ERAC (Engin de Reconnaissance Amphibie de Combat), in the 1960s, it was eventually decided to continue its development in the form of vehicles for two distinct functions: an armoured personnel carrier and a heavy reconnaissance vehicle to succeed the EBR. The French have always been ready to consider either wheeled or tracked vehicles for most combat functions below that of main battle tank, and the AMX-10 family which followed the ERAC was developed in closely-related wheeled and tracked versions. The earliest of these, in both wheeled and tracked forms, were armoured personnel carriers and ultimately the tracked model, AMX-10P, was chosen to go into production for the French army as the replacement for the AMX-13 Véhicule de Combat d'Infanterie.

Development of the wheeled vehicle, AMX-10R (R signifies *roues*, or wheels), was continued, not ultimately as an armoured personnel carrier, but, with lower hull, revised glacis plate and mounting a 105-mm gun turret, as a heavy armoured car, the AMX-10RC (RC means *roues canon*). Three prototype chassis were completed by December 1973 and the first 105-mm gun turret was also received near the end of the same year; the other two turrets followed in 1974.

Development work continued until 1977, when series production for the French army commenced, with 190 vehicles due to be delivered by 1982 and to be followed by a further batch of 160.

The AMX-10RC is a compact six-wheeled vehicle, the wheels being equally spaced, with a low turret forward of centre mounting a long 105-mm gun. The driver's position is at the left-hand side near the front and is protected by a cupola hatch which can be swung away to the right when the vehicle is not in combat. This cupola has three periscopic vision blocks; passive light-intensification or infra-red equipment for night driving can be fitted. The turret contains the other three members of the crew: the commander on the right, the gunner behind the commander,

PLATE 26
AMX-10RC
FRANCE

and the loader on the left. The loader is also the radio operator and has basic driving controls for driving in reverse in emergencies.

The engine is the same as that of the tracked AMX-10C, namely an Hispano-Suiza type HS 115 eight-cylinder water-cooled diesel developing 280 h.p. at 3,000 r.p.m. The AMX-10RC's torque converter preselective gearbox and steering differential are also the same as those of its tracked counterpart, although transmission shafts either side of the hull inside the armour are needed to carry the power to the six wheels. The wheels are not steerable, skid-steering being achieved through the differential steering system, but the ground clearance of the hull can be adjusted up or down by means of the oleo-pneumatic suspension system. This has the advantage of giving the vehicle either a relatively high ground clearance for crossing rough terrain or the minimum height when in action.

The performance of the AMX-10RC compares well with that of the tracked AMX-10C, maxi-

mum road speed being claimed as being 10 km/h faster at 85 km/h. The average cross-country speed for both AMX-10RC and AMX-10C is quoted as 40 km/h, although the wheeled vehicle in the worst conditions is likely to be inferior. The two types are also similar in manoeuvrability, although at the expense of heavy tyre wear by the AMX-10RC on hard surfaces.

Another point shared with the AMX-10C is the ability to swim without preparation, propulsion in water being by two hydrojets in the rear of the hull. A trim vane is normally kept folded on the front glacis plate. The maximum water speed is 7.2 km/h.

The AMX-10RC's armament consists of a 105-mm gun and a coaxial 7.62-mm machine gun mounted in the turret. Fin-stabilised ammunition for the 105-mm gun is either armour piercing, with a muzzle velocity of 1,090 m/s capable of penetrating 350 mm of vertical steel armour, or high explosive, which is a heavier projectile with a lower muzzle velocity of 800 m/s.

AMX-10RC

Germany, Democratic Republic

SK-1 and SK-2 Plates 27 and 28

The SK-1, a light armoured car, is one of the few armoured vehicles designed as well as built in East Germany. Dating from 1954, the SK-1 was intended for internal security duties and border patrol with the paramilitary police and militia units. The chassis is a modified version of the two-ton, 4 × 4, Robur 30K truck, supplied by VEB-Automobilwerk Robur of Zittau in Saxony. It has a four-cylinder air-cooled engine developing 55 h.p. at 2,800 r.p.m. The design of the armoured hull is derived from that of German

World War 2 armoured cars and, more immediately, the Soviet BA-64 light armoured car.

It has a crew of five and is armed with a machine gun in a hand-traversed turret that is exceptionally well provided with observation ports. Only a relatively small number of cars of this type was built and they are not likely to remain in service much longer.

An internal security vehicle, the SK-2 consists of a G-5 6 × 6 lorry with a lightly-armoured cab surmounted by a water cannon (with a maximum

SK-1 armoured cars on patrol

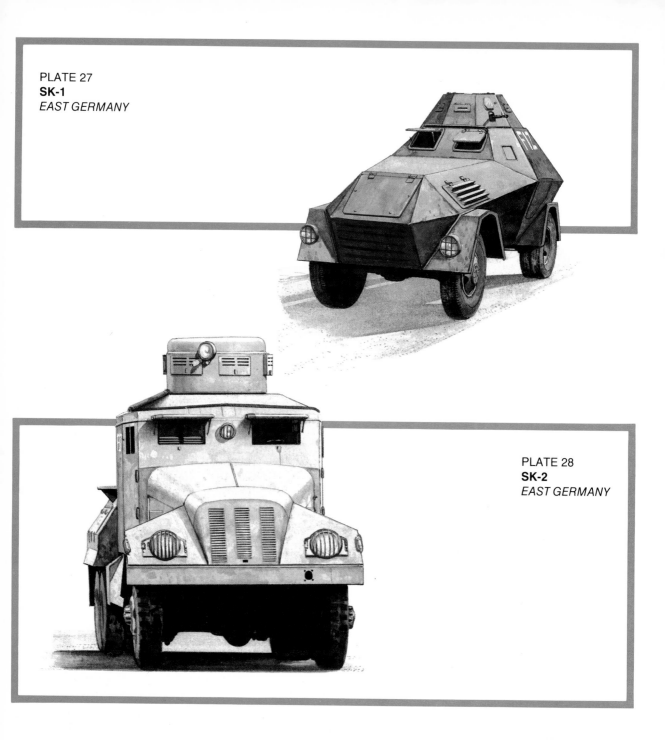

PLATE 27
SK-1
EAST GERMANY

PLATE 28
SK-2
EAST GERMANY

range of 70 metres) in a revolving turret. A water tank at the rear of the vehicle contains 4,000 litres of water. Carrying a crew of three men, the SK-2 can remain in action for long periods, provided it has access to water points in the street, because the water tank can be refilled from inside the vehicle within five to ten minutes.

The G-5 truck (originally known as Horch) supplied by VEB Kraftfahrzeugwerke Ernst Grube has a six-cylinder, water-cooled diesel engine developing 120 h.p. at 2,000 r.p.m. which, in this version, gives it a speed of just under 50 km/h.

Germany, Federal Republic

Transportpanzer 1 Plates 29 and 30

Both armoured and unarmoured transport vehicles
were envisaged, together with an eight-wheeled
reconnaissance vehicle, in the programme of
re-equipment for the Bundeswehr in the 1970s
and 1980s. In competition with a consortium
known as GB (short for Gemeinschaftsbüro),
Daimler-Benz's designs for six-wheeled and four-
wheeled armoured transport vehicles were accepted as well as that for the reconnaissance car
(Spähpanzer 2 Luchs). For the record, the GB

consortium won the contract for the whole range
of unarmoured trucks.

The successful Daimler-Benz six-wheeled armoured transport vehicle has the wheels closely
spaced with a slightly larger gap between the second and third pairs, unlike some of the prototypes which had the rear pair well separated
from the others. It has rigid axles with coil springs
and hydraulic shock absorbers which are identical
to those of Spähpanzer 2, like many of the other

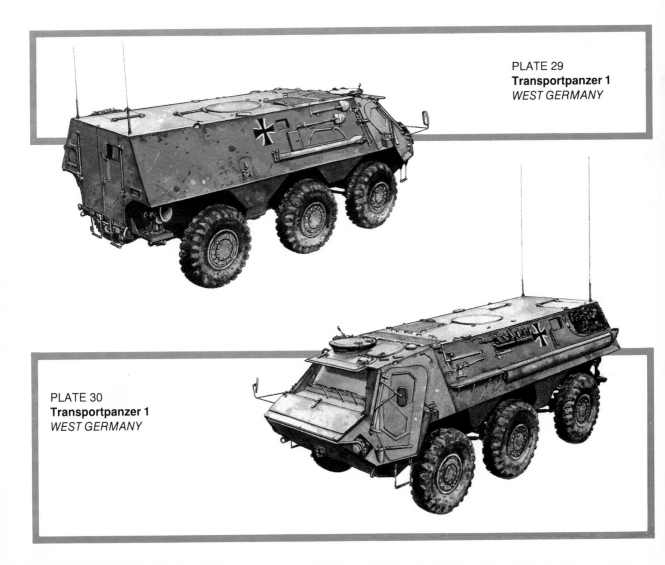

PLATE 29
Transportpanzer 1
WEST GERMANY

PLATE 30
Transportpanzer 1
WEST GERMANY

components. Only the front four wheels are steerable. The engine is located immediately behind the driver's compartment and the power is taken, via transfer boxes, forward to the front pair of wheels and back to the centre and rear pairs. It is a multi-fuel Daimler-Benz Type OM-402A V-8 water-cooled engine developing 320 h.p. at 2,500 r.p.m. A feature of the design, in common with other modern German armoured vehicles, is that the engine can be removed quickly from the vehicle for servicing, having only a single electri-

cal plug connection and quick self-sealing connections on all fluid lines. The gearbox is a ZF 4HP 500-1 six-speed automatic.

The TPz 1 is fully amphibious, water propulsion being by means of two propellers at the rear, which can be swivelled for steering, driven from the main engine. An hydraulically-erected trimboard is carried on the glacis plate. The maximum speeds attainable are 10 km/h in water and 90 km/h on roads.

The Transportpanzer's hull is of welded steel.

Transportpanzer 1. One of the water propellers at the rear shows clearly in this view

The front compartment contains the driver, on the left, and the vehicle commander. The rear compartment, behind the engine, has seats, facing inwards, for 10 personnel. A tunnel alongside the engine on the right-hand side provides access between the front and rear compartments. There is a firing port on either side of the hull and one in the right-hand door at the rear. Both the commander and the driver have roof hatches and there is a large circular roof hatch at the front end of the rear compartment in which a 7.62-mm machine gun or a 20-mm cannon can be mounted.

Just under 1,000 Transportpanzer 1s have been built and are employed as armoured personnel carriers with Bundeswehr anti-aircraft units (equipped with Gepard anti-aircraft gun tanks and Roland surface-to-air missile carriers), N.B.C. (nuclear, biological, chemical warfare) defence units, signals units, engineering units, supply transport units, and as carriers for battlefield surveillance radar.

Amphibisches Pionier — Erkundungs-fahrzeug (APE) Plate 31

In the competition for a four-wheeled four-wheel-drive armoured transport vehicle, Transportpanzer 2 (TPz 2), the Daimler-Benz design, was chosen, together with that for the 6 × 6 TPz 1. Whereas the latter was put into production, the TPz 2 project was shelved after prototypes had been built and tested. It had a high number of automotive components in common with both the TPz 1 and the eight-wheeled Spähpanzer 2 Luchs, and its hull was a shortened version of its 6 × 6 partner.

The Transportpanzer 2 was, in effect, revived later in a different form when Daimler-Benz went into partnership with Eisenwerke Kaiserslautern Göppner GmbH (EWK). In 1964 EWK developed an all-terrain amphibious 4 × 4 test vehicle, known as P3, which proved to have an excellent performance and had features that would be suitable for an engineer reconnaissance vehicle, one of the planned functions of Transportpanzer 2.

The APE consists of a modified version of the running gear of the P3 test vehicle, but the original 170-h.p. engine was replaced by a 320-h.p. Daimler-Benz engine, like that of Transportpanzer 1, and a shortened version of the hull of that vehicle. The much lighter weight of the APE compared with Transportpanzer 1, together with a better hull configuration, improved layout of the water propellers, and large section tyres (the pressure of which can be varied in motion to suit the terrain and higher ground clearance) give it a superior cross-country and water performance. This is needed particularly in a vehicle with the prime purpose of reconnoitring river crossings and other military engineering undertakings. It can descend steep river banks or climb out of the water and up soft ground and, by adjusting the tyre pressures, cross marshy terrain.

The interior hull arrangement of the APE is very much like that of Transportpanzer 1, with the driver and commander at the front, the engine in the centre and the compartment for equipment or, as a personnel carrier, 10 to 12 personnel at the rear. Two doors are provided in the hull rear plate, two hatches in the roof, for the driver and commander, and three hatches in the rear compartment, one of which can be used for mounting a 20-mm cannon. Six angled smoke cannister dischargers are carried on the left side of the hull. On roads the APE can cruise at 80 km/h and in water 12 km/h can be attained.

Spähpanzer 2 Luchs Plates 32 and 33

The Luchs (Lynx) is the latest manifestation of a German tradition of eight-wheeled reconnaissance vehicles going back as far as 1929. In that year, eight-wheeled protype armoured cars had been completed by the firms of C. D. Magirus and Daimler-Benz (and Büssing-N.A.G. had built a ten-wheeler). Although none of these prototypes went into production because of their relatively high cost, further research work was started in 1935 by Büssing-N.A.G. and resulted in the Schwerer Panzerspähwagen (8 rad) SdKfz 231. This vehicle, with an improved version, the SdKfz 234, was built in different models throughout World War 2.

Some 30 years after the initial work on the SdKfz 231 (8 rad), drawings were started on a new eight-wheeled reconnaissance vehicle for the army of the German Federal Republic. Two

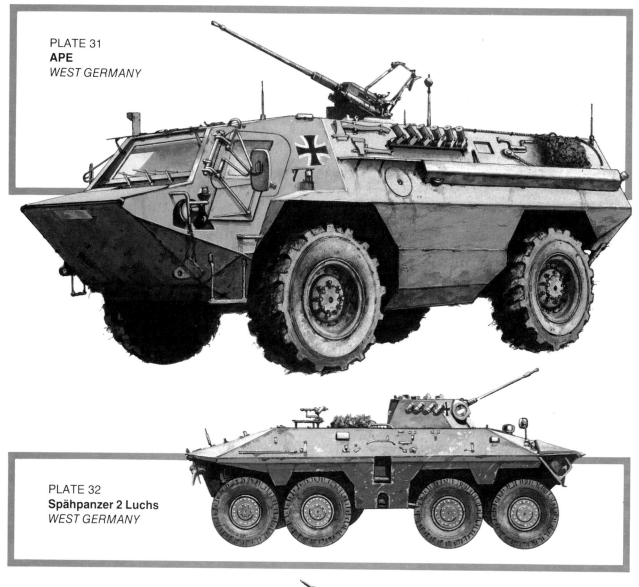

PLATE 31
APE
WEST GERMANY

PLATE 32
Spähpanzer 2 Luchs
WEST GERMANY

PLATE 33
Spähpanzer 2 Luchs
WEST GERMANY

groups were involved: a consortium (known as Gemeinschaftsbüro, or GB for short) consisting of five firms (including Büssing) on the one hand, and Daimler-Benz on the other. Seven protypes were built by GB and six by Daimler-Benz. Exhaustive tests were carried out in Norway and Sardinia as well as in West Germany itself and the Daimler-Benz version was chosen, although Rheinstahl (now Thyssen-Henschel), a member of GB, was awarded the overall contract for series production.

An all-welded form of construction has been adopted for the hull of the Luchs, which is fully waterproofed. The eight wheels are mounted on four rigid axles sprung on coil springs, with vertical shock absorbers, giving good ground adhesion for this type of suspension. All eight wheels are steerable so that the minimum turning circle is only 11.5 metres. All the wheels are also driven, although for high speeds on roads transmission can be limited to four wheels only. The engine is situated on the right-hand side above and just forward of the third pair of wheels, and is a Daimler-Benz Type OM-403VA V-10 developing 390 h.p. on diesel fuel. The engine will also run on petrol, although with a reduced output. The transmission is a fully automatic ZF type 4PW95-1 giving four forward speeds and four in reverse with a top speed of 90 km/h in either direction. In order to take full advantage of this performance, the radio operator is situated behind the engine on the left side of the hull and provided with a second set of driving controls for driving backwards in emergencies. The normal driver is seated at the front of the vehicle on the left-hand side behind the low sloping glacis plate. Behind him is the fighting compartment surmounted by the turret containing the vehicle commander on the left and the gunner on the right. The primary armament is a 20-mm cannon, a Rheinmetall Mk20 Rh 202, in the turret with an elevation of up to 70 degrees, a depression of minus 20 degrees and 360 degrees traverse so that it can be used against aerial as well as ground targets. A searchlight for infra-red or white light is mounted on the left-hand side of the turret and can be operated coaxially with the 20-mm gun. A 7.62-mm machine gun is carried on an open mounting over the commander's hatch on the turret roof.

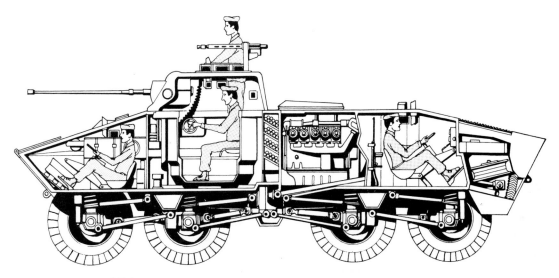

The prototype Luchs, LG494

For operation in water the Luchs is driven by two propellers at the rear which can be swivelled for steering. The water speed is 10 km/h. An hydraulically-erected trimboard is carried on the glacis plate; when folded it provides some extra protection against hollow charge projectiles.

Four hundred and eight Spähpanzer 2 Luchs were built between 1975 and 1977 for the Bundeswehr and are in service.

Spähpanzer 2 Luchs

Transportpanzer UR-416
Plates 34 and 35

An armoured personnel carrier in its basic version, but adaptable to varied roles, the UR-416 is in use in many countries and some 700 have been built. Part of the reason for this success is the use of the well-tried Daimler-Benz Unimog truck chassis. To this has been added an all-welded steel hull designed by Rheinstahl (now Thyssen-

Henschel, the UR-416's manufacturer) as a unit. An interesting feature is that the hull can be lifted from the chassis, which remains mechanically complete and can be driven away. This operation is carried out by unfastening the four couplings attaching the hull to the chassis frame and the one electrical connection, and lifting the hull with a 2,000 kg crane. Alternatively, the hull can be raised by the use of three jacks, which can be carried in the vehicle, if necessary. Two jacks are positioned at the sides and one at the rear and the hull is lifted, higher at the front to clear the engine, so that the chassis can be driven forwards from under the hull.

The Unimog chassis has a fairly standard layout for a four-wheel-drive commercial vehicle, with a front-mounted engine (Daimler-Benz DB-OM352 six-cylinder in-line diesel developing 110 h.p. at 2,800 r.p.m.), a six-speed gearbox (or optionally one with eight forward speeds and four reverse) and a centrally-located transfer box from which cardan shafts lead to rigid axles at the front and rear. On the road it is driven by rear wheels alone, but for cross-country work four-wheel drive can be engaged and the differentials locked while on the move.

The hull has nine-mm armour, proof against small arms, and has room for 10 in its standard personnel-carrying configuration. The driver sits at the front on the left side with the vehicle commander on the right. Behind them six personnel sit facing outwards and two sit facing rearwards. Five firing ports are provided on each side and there are two in the rear plate on either side of the spare wheel, which is normally mounted in this position. There are two hatches in the roof, a rectangular one near the rear and a circular one in which a machine gun can be mounted on a ring mounting. Three doors are provided, one each side and one at the rear. They are in two parts, the lower of which opens downwards for use as a step.

Weighing 6,300 kg loaded, the UR-416 has a maximum speed of 80 km/h. In addition to the standard armoured personnel carrier version, the UR-416 is available as a command vehicle (with communications equipment and a crew of four), an ambulance (four stretchers or eight sitting patients), or a reconnaissance vehicle with a turret mounted in place of the circular hatch and either single or twin machine guns, a 20-mm cannon, or a 90-mm recoilless gun. The COBRA anti-tank system with eight missiles can be carried, or alternatively the TOW system in a retractable mounting, together with 11 missiles. Multiple smoke dischargers can also be added.

As well as being employed by the military and paramilitary forces of many countries, the UR-416 is also used as a police vehicle, in which version two types of observation cupola are available, together with a dozer blade for clearing obstacles.

Transportpanzer UR-416

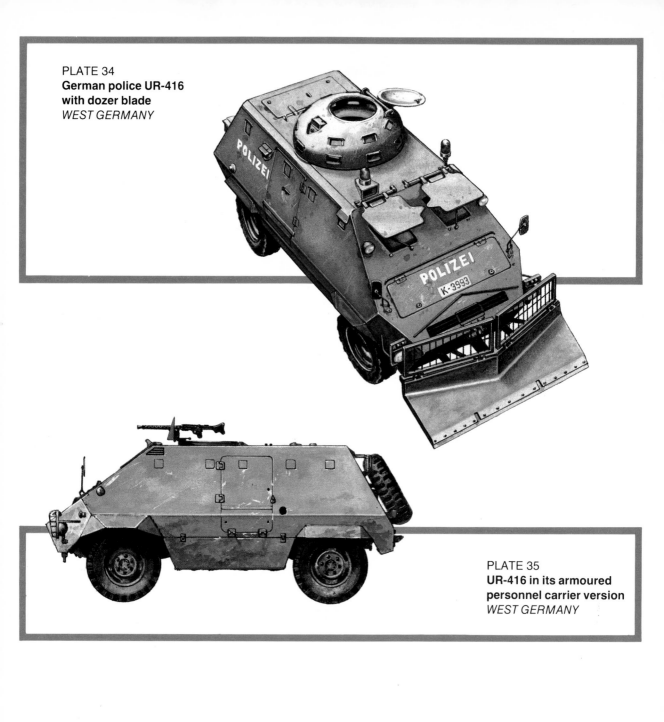

PLATE 34
**German police UR-416
with dozer blade**
WEST GERMANY

POLIZEI

POLIZEI
K·3993

PLATE 35
**UR-416 in its armoured
personnel carrier version**
WEST GERMANY

Hungary

FUG (OT 65) and FUG-70 (OT 66)
Plates 36 and 37

These light multipurpose armoured vehicles were developed by Hungary to take the place of comparable Soviet vehicles. Although not allowed by the Soviet Union to produce their own heavy armour, the Warsaw Pact countries have been able to design and build armoured cars and other supporting vehicles. Hungary has a long tradition in the evolution of armoured cars, going back to 1915 and, more importantly, Nicholas Sraussler's designs of the 1930s that were produced in both Hungary and the United Kingdom and saw service in World War 2.

PLATE 36
FUG (OT 65)
HUNGARY

PLATE 37
FUG-70 (OT 66)
HUNGARY

First appearing in the early 1960s, the FUG (Felderítö Úszó Gépkoczi, or amphibious reconnaissance car) was derived from the Soviet BRDM. Designed for, and achieving, a better performance than its Soviet prototype, the FUG has some features and an overall resemblance in common with the BRDM. The most notable shared characteristic is the four auxiliary wheels which can be lowered and driven by a power take-off from the engine to greatly increase the FUG's cross-country and obstacle-surmounting performance. Although there is a family likeness in the hull, the FUG, unlike the BRDM, has a rear-mounted engine, the Csepel D-414.44 four-cylinder in-line water-cooled diesel developing 100 h.p. at 2,300 r.p.m. This gives it a road speed of 87 km/h. The all-welded hull is fully waterproofed and twin hydrojets at the rear give it a speed of about nine km/h in water.

The crew compartment is towards the front of the vehicle and although as a scout car the crew would consist of two or three, the total capacity as a personnel carrier is five. There are six firing ports in the hull sides and rear. Apart from the small number of troops carried, the design is hardly ideal for assault purposes since access is only via twin hatches in the hull roof.

A new model of FUG appeared in 1966 and was called FUG-66. It had a fully enclosed, redesigned hull with a small streamlined turret mounting a heavy machine gun and a 7.62-mm machine gun. This vehicle appears to have been built only in small numbers and was the development model for the FUG-70 which was in full-scale production four years later.

A major mechanical difference between FUG-70 and the original FUG is the elimination of the four auxiliary wheels, and the space gained, together with the new design of the upper hull, enables six men to be carried in addition to the basic crew of three. As the overall dimensions remain the same accommodation must be very cramped.

The turret of the FUG-70 mounts a 14.5-mm and a 7.62-mm machine gun and has an open top. A Hungarian-built German six-cylinder in-line diesel engine, the water-cooled Raba-MAN D-2156 developing 120 h.p., gives a maximum road speed of 100 km/h and a slightly increased water speed, although the lack of the belly wheels must lower the overall cross-country performance.

Although the full Hungarian designations of all versions of the FUG are not known, the Czechs, who are also major users of this type, have designated the original FUG and the FUG-70, respectively, Obrneny Transporter OT 65 and OT 66. There are a number of variants in service, including a Czech ambulance version of the OT 65 and one (OT 65A) with a turret mounting a 7.62-mm machine gun and an 82-mm recoilless rifle. There are chemical decontamination versions of both FUG models and a turretless command vehicle based on the FUG-70.

FUG (OT 65)

Irish Republic/Belgium

Timoney-BDX Armoured Personnel
Carrier Plates 38 and 39

The small army of the Irish Republic is one that has always relied on wheeled armoured vehicles more than most, and it is perhaps appropriate that a wheeled armoured personnel carrier developed in the Irish Republic should be having success in overseas sales. At the request in the early 1970s of the Irish Department of Defence, Professor S. G. Timoney (who earlier had been involved in Britain in the development of the Saladin and Saracen wheeled A.F.V.s) designed a wheeled armoured personnel carrier for possible adoption by the Irish Army. This work was carried out under the aegis of Technology Investments Ltd (T.I.L.) of Dublin, an engineering research and development company of which Professor Timoney and his brother are directors.

The first prototype was completed in July 1973, only some 18 months after design work commenced. Two more prototypes were completed during the following year, followed by a small batch of preproduction vehicles. While the proto-

types were under test by the Irish army in 1975 they were inspected by representatives of the Belgian defence ministry, which was then evaluating wheeled armoured personnel carriers of different countries with a view to selecting one to re-equip the Belgian Gendarmerie and air force for the defence of air bases etc. Shortly afterwards, in the same year, the Belgian firm of Beherman Demoen, wishing to enter the military equipment field, obtained a production licence for the Timoney armoured personnel carrier from its manufacturers, T.I.L.

This step, added to the intrinsic merits of the Timoney vehicle, placed it in a strong position to gain the order for the Belgian services, and after three months of trials in 1976 by the Direction de la Force Terrestre, Division Méchanique Etablissement No. 1 at Brasschaat, a production contract was finally placed with Beherman Demoen. This called for 80 vehicles for the Belgian Gendarmerie, some to be armoured personnel carriers (26

Timoney-BDX armoured personnel carrier with twin 7.62-mm machine-gun turret

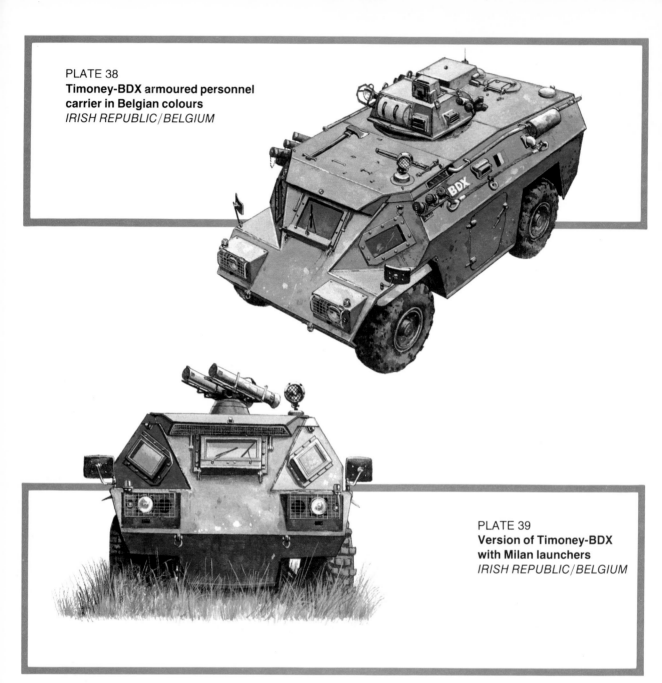

PLATE 38
**Timoney-BDX armoured personnel
carrier in Belgian colours**
IRISH REPUBLIC / BELGIUM

PLATE 39
**Version of Timoney-BDX
with Milan launchers**
IRISH REPUBLIC / BELGIUM

fitted with dozer blades) and others as mortar
carriers, and 43 armoured personnel carriers for
the air force. A much larger order (of around
1,000) for the Belgian army is reported, as well as
a smaller one of 200 for the Irish army. Some
African, South American and Asian countries are
also considering placing orders.

The Timoney-BDX armoured personnel carrier was designed to be used in urban internal
security or normal military operations to carry up

to 12 personnel and have a good road and cross-
country performance. At the same time, with an
eye to sales in countries without highly developed
industrial capacity, it was to be relatively simple
and to use existing commercial components as far
as possible.

The hull of the Timoney-BDX is a box made of
welded hard steel plates; the upper sections of the
sides slope inwards and there is a triangular glacis
plate at the front. The rear plates contain a large

single door. The belly plates are angled for mine-blast deflection, and the protection as a whole is of the higher degree necessary in a vehicle likely to be engaged in urban anti-guerilla operations. It will withstand 7.62-mm armour-piercing bullets fired at short range. A relatively large laminated glass windscreen is provided for the driver, together with two similar, but smaller, vision ports in the angled corner plates on each side. The centre windscreen can be opened forwards for use as an emergency exit. All three laminated glass windows give the same degree of protection as the steel armour. The hull sides each have a door, and in the prototype there were three upward-opening small arms ports on the left side and two on the right. Two further ports were located in the rear plate on either side of the door. In the later preproduction model of the Timoney-BDX armoured personnel carrier, however, the ports have been replaced by ball-mountings with vision blocks above them, one mounting on each side and one in the rear door. A circular hatch is provided in the roof at the back end and there is provision for a small turret or ring mounting in the centre. The roof was flat in the prototype but a

slope on the rear half was introduced in later vehicles to give the turret machine gun a better field of fire over the rear. As an alternative to the turret, two large outward-opening roof hatches can be provided.

The standard power plant of the Timoney-BDX is a Chrysler 360 CID series V-8 water-cooled petrol engine developing 200 h.p. at 4,000 r.p.m. This is a widely known unit, since it is used in the ubiquitous American M113 tracked armoured personnel carrier, but a diesel engine is an alternative. The engine air intake is at the top edge of the glacis plate above the driver's head; the hood incorporates a hinged flame trap to guard against flammable missiles thrown at the vehicle. The uninsulated exhaust pipes are located along each side of the top edge of the hull to deter urban guerillas from clambering aboard. The gearbox is an Allison AT 540 fully-automatic type, with four forward speeds and one reverse. The engine is located to the right of the centre line just behind the front wheels and behind it is the gearbox from which the transmission is led to a two-speed transfer box and thence to the back wheels. Another drive shaft, which can be

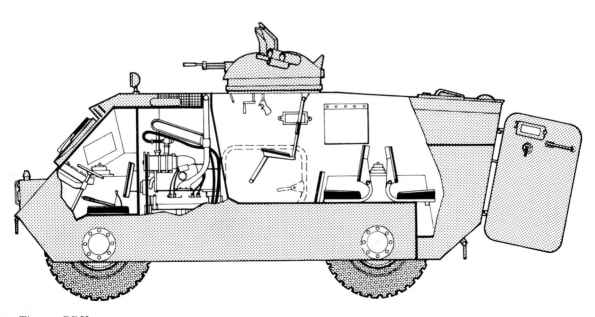

Timoney-BDX

disengaged, leads forward on the left side of the engine to the front wheels. There is independent suspension on all four wheels, which are carried on twin transverse wishbone units controlled by a coil spring and hydraulic shock absorber at each position.

The wheels are fitted with 11.00×20 or 12.00×20 run-flat tyres. Internally, the Timoney-BDX has the driver's compartment at the front, with the engine behind the driver and access to the main crew compartment at the left. In addition to the driver, nine personnel (eleven in the prototype) can be carried seated in various arrangements of transverse and outward-facing seats and there is a suspended seat for the gunner when a turret is fitted.

In addition to the armoured personnel carrier versions, with or without a machine gun turret or ring mounting, the Timoney-BDX is available with twin launchers for the Milan missile, as an 81-mm motor carrier (with the mortar mounted in the crew compartment), or with various turrets for guns between 20 and 90 mm in calibre. Professor Timoney has also proposed a six-wheeled version (so developing a family like those of some of the French manufacturers) for which an oscillating 75- or 90-mm gun turret would be one option.

Israel

Ram V-1 Light Armoured Reconnaissance Vehicle
Plates 40 and 41

Known as the Ramta RBY-Mk 1 when it first appeared in 1975, the Ram V-1's designers must have been able to draw on the wide battle experience in Israel in the operation of a variety of light armoured vehicles. American armoured half-tracks have been among the most important of these, but various other foreign captured as well as purchased vehicles have been employed by the Israeli army. Two leading features of the Ram V-1, a light armoured reconnaissance and patrol vehicle, are a good cross-country performance and the ability to protect its crew against mine damage.

The engine, mounted at the rear, is a standard American-designed Dodge 225-2 six-cylinder petrol model; it is water-cooled and develops 120 b.h.p. Like the engine, all the other automotive parts used for the Ram V-1 are claimed to be commercially available components. The gearbox is a 'new process' 435 manual four-speed type,

linked to a 'new process' transfer case, from which the transmission is led forwards and backwards to 'solid' axles. The suspension is on conventional longitudinal semi-elliptic springs (six leaves at the front and four at the rear) and hydraulic shock absorbers. The monocoque, all-welded armoured hull is practically independent of the engine, transmission and suspension and, as there is a relatively long wheelbase, no part of the hull occupied by the crew is over the wheels. The engine cover is fibre glass, as are the mudguards. The hull is made up from sloping 8-mm hardened steel plate for its upper parts and 10-mm non-hardened steel for the V-shaped under surfaces. The spare wheel is normally mounted flat over the front axle, where it adds to the frontal protection, but an alternative mounting is upright at the back of the engine compartment.

The crew are all in close contact, the driver being on the left, the commander on the right, and six personnel behind them sitting back to back facing outwards. The driver and commander have large forward-facing vision ports as well as side ports, all upward opening (unlike the early prototype vehicle in which there were sliding-opening vision ports and other minor differences from the current model). There are no other vision or firing ports in the hull and no doors, thus

RAM V-1 fitted with turret mounting twin 20-mm anti-aircraft cannon

PLATE 40
RAM V-1
ISRAEL

PLATE 41
**Later version
of RAM V-1**
ISRAEL

making for a stronger structure. Access is via the open top of the hull, around the upper edge of which can be attached up to four pintle mountings for machine guns. It seems improbable, however, that as many as the four 0.30-in. Browning machine guns shown being manned simultaneously in publicity photographs would be carried in practice. Alternative armament for the Ram V-1 is twin 20-mm cannon, the TOW anti-tank missile launcher, or a 106-mm recoilless rifle. For the latter mounting, provision is made for lowering the whole driver's/commander's frontal plate forwards.

With operation in open desert terrain envisaged, some of the Ram V-1's characteristics are as follows. Maximum height to the top of the hull is only 1.66 metres and ground clearance (excluding differential casings) is 0.375 metres. The maximum road speed is 95 km/h and 60 km/h over rough terrain is claimed. With a 140-litre fuel tank, the road range is 550 km off roads. The latest version has increased fuel capacity giving a maximum range of 850 km. A winch with 2,722 kg capacity is provided.

Produced by the Ramta Structures and Systems division of Israel Aircraft Industries, the Ram V-1 is not known to be in use, so far, outside the country of its origin.

A new version of the Ram V-1 is a fully enclosed reconnaissance car. Known as Ram V-2, this has a 12.7-mm machine gun mounting on the commander's cupola. A further variant is an anti-aircraft vehicle mounting a turret armed with twin 20-mm cannon.

Italy

Fiat 6614 Armoured Personnel Carrier and Fiat 6616 Armoured Car
Plates 42 and 43

Although Italy was one of the first countries to build armoured cars and test them out in active service conditions (in North Africa in 1912) and subsequently produced several good designs right up to the end of World War 2, it was not until some 20 years after that conflict that work began again on an Italian wheeled armoured vehicle.

Fiat of Turin began design work in the late 1960s for a family of light 4 × 4 armoured vehi-

cles using common automotive and other component parts as far as possible, and including a personnel carrier and a reconnaissance car. The former, designated Fiat 6614, was the first to appear.

The layout adopted for the armoured personnel carrier was that commonly used to give an unobstructed rear compartment and a full-sized rear door. The engine is at the front (on the right-hand side) with the driver next to it and the personnel compartment behind. In the original version (6614 BM) only six personnel could be carried in addition to the driver, but the later model, Fiat 6614 CM, in which the 115-h.p. petrol engine was replaced by a more powerful diesel, the hull was enlarged to take nine in the rear compartment. Further changes, resulting in the definitive model

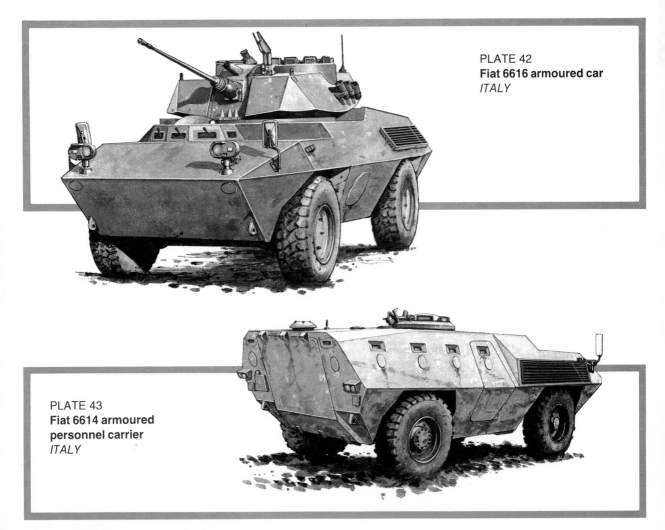

PLATE 42
Fiat 6616 armoured car
ITALY

PLATE 43
Fiat 6614 armoured personnel carrier
ITALY

that has gone into production, include an uprating of the engine, a Fiat type 8062.24 six-cylinder in-line diesel, to give 160 h.p. instead of 130 h.p., and a further seat to increase the capacity to 11 including the driver. External differences include the engine grilles, which originally were on the top of the engine compartment and are now in the sides of the hull, and the two square roof hatches, which replace the former single round hatch at the back of the rear compartment. The large power-operated downward-opening rear door now lacks the two ports, which have been transferred to the rear plate of the hull either side of the door. For small arms there are 10 circular firing ports below bullet proof glass vision blocks; eight are in the sides (two of them incorporated in the side doors) and two are in the rear plate. In the centre of the roof is a rotating cupola for the vehicle commander with five periscopes and a pintle mounting for a 12.7-mm machine gun or, alternatively, lighter or heavier weapons from 7.62 mm to 20 mm. The driver has five vision blocks and a circular roof hatch. Ambulance and cargo-carrying versions of the Fiat 6614 are available, as well as the personnel carrier.

The Fiat 6614 CM weighs 8.5 tons loaded and has a maximum speed of 96 km/h. It is fully amphibious without preparation and can attain a speed of 4.5 km/h in water, propelled by its road wheels.

A large production order for the supply of 6614s for Peru was cancelled with a change of government in that country, but a batch was supplied to South Korea and some, at least, were in service there by 1979.

The Fiat 6616 armoured car prototype appeared in the early 1970s, after the 6614. It has many automotive components in common with the armoured personnel carrier including, in the latest versions of both types, the identical model of engine, the Fiat type 8062.24 160 h.p. diesel. Although sharing the same 'family', Fiat's policy has been to design a different hull for the armoured car, so as to give it the optimum ballistic and operational performance for its reconnaissance role. The hull is accordingly lower than that of the personnel carrier and is a very clean design. Without the need for a rear door, the engine is located at the back. The driver has similar vision arrangements to those in the Fiat

Fiat 6614 armoured personnel carrier

6614 but is positioned to the right of the centre line. The turret, designed by the Oto Melara firm, is in the approximate centre of the vehicle and contains the other two crew members. The commander, seated at the left, has a roof hatch which incorporates nine periscopes for all-round vision, and the gunner, at the right side of the turret, has a single sighting and observation periscope on the turret roof in front of his roof hatch.

The main armament is a 20-mm Mk 20 Rh 202 cannon of German design, built under licence in Italy by Whitehead Moto Fides of Leghorn. The secondary armament, a 7.62-mm MG 42/59 machine gun, is unusual in that it is mounted coaxially above the 20-mm cannon. A grenade launcher for high explosive, smoke or anti-personnel bombs is mounted in the roof of the gunner's hatch and can be loaded and fired from inside the vehicle, and there are six (three each side) smoke grenade launchers mounted on the turret sides. These are of German design and are also used on the Leopard tanks in service with the Italian army. To complete the armament a 7.62-mm machine gun, fired by the vehicle commander, can be carried on a pintle mounting on the turret roof.

The Fiat 6616, like the 6614 personnel carrier, has gone through several stages of design since it first appeared. The main changes in the 6616 BM were to the engine compartment, which had its roof raised to accommodate a larger engine and side grilles added, and the turret, which had some changes in contour and, among other things, the removal of the grenade launcher from the commander's hatch to that of the gunner.

A twin 20-mm anti-aircraft gun turret or the French 90-mm gun turret used on the AML H-90 armoured car can be fitted to the Fiat 6616, and a further development is a version with a lengthened hull fitted with an Anglo-Belgian Scorpion tank turret armed with a Cockerill 90-mm gun. Weighing 7,950 kg, the Fiat 6616 has a maximum road speed of 100 km/h and, like the 6614, is fully amphibious with a water speed, propelled by its wheels, of five km/h.

The first production order for the Fiat 6616 was a batch of 50 for the Italian forces, of which 30 were for the Carabinieri and 20 for the army for evaluation by reconnaissance units. Foreign orders have been received from South Korea, where it is being built under licence, and Somalia. The vehicles for the latter country include special modifications such as a spare tyre and crew compartment ventilation and engine air intake filters suited to operation in tropical conditions.

Support version of the Fiat 6616 armoured car fitted with a 90-mm Cockerill gun

Netherlands

Pantserwagen Infanterie YP-408

Unique among modern armoured vehicles in being eight-wheeled with only six wheels driven, the YP-408 was developed by Van Doorne's Automobielfabriken N-V (DAF) in conjunction with the Dutch army, from the earlier YA-328 6 × 6 truck by the same manufacturer. The first prototype was built in 1958, following about two years of design work and the production of a mock-up. This experimental vehicle was powered by an American 133-h.p. Hercules JXLD six-cylinder engine, like the YA-328 truck, and differed externally from the series production models in having a different shaped engine compartment, with grilles, angled roof hatches at the rear and

other minor points. The design was accepted, with modifications, and between 1964 and 1968 about 750 YP-408s were built for the Royal Netherlands Army and are still in service.

The YP-408 in its standard version is an armoured personnel carrier known as PWI-S(GR) or Pantserwagen Infanterie-Standaard (Groep) for carrying 10 infantrymen with their personal equipment, together with the vehicle driver and commander/gunner. This basic model is supplemented by five variants all externally similar, as follows.

The PWI-S(PC), the infantry platoon commander's vehicle, carries only six infantrymen in addition to the platoon commander and vehicle crew of two (driver and gunner) but has extra radio equipment.

The PWCO, a command vehicle for company or battalion commanders, has extra radios and a folding table and map shelf to facilitate the com-

Pantserwagen Infanterie YP-408 PWI-S (GR), the basic version, carrys 12 personnel

Panterserwagen Infanterie YP-408 PWI-S (PC),
the platoon commander's version carrying nine troops

mand of an infantry unit in the field. In addition to the operating crew of two, the PWCO normally carries the infantry commander and three members of his headquarters staff. A tent extension can be added to the rear of the hull to increase the working space, or for order groups etc. The PWCO (and also the platoon commander's model PWI-S(PC)) has an extra fully-rotating periscope, with ×3 magnification, towards the rear of the hull roof.

The PW-GWT is an armoured ambulance lacking the machine gun mounting of the other vehicles of the series which can carry two stretcher cases and four sitting cases. The crew consists of the driver and two medical orderlies.

The PW-V is a cargo carrier for 1,500 kg of stores and is operated by a crew of two. It can be

Company commander's version of the Pantserwagen Infanterie YP-408, PWCO, carries six personnel

Pantserwagen Infanterie YP-408 PW-GWT, the ambulance version

Pantserwagen Infanterie YP-408 PW-MT carries seven personnel and tows the 120-mm mortar, shown set up on the left

converted into an ambulance, although the gun mounting would have to be removed and a radio (not normally carried in the PW-V) fitted.

The PW-MT, an armoured tractor for the Brandt 120-mm mortar, differs externally from the other versions chiefly in having slightly smaller doors on which the lower outer corners are mitred to clear the mortar when it is attached to the vehicle's towing hook. Fifty rounds for the mortar are carried, together with the mortar crew of five and the vehicle driver and commander/gunner.

The YP-408 has an all-welded hull with armour between 8 and 15 mm. The engine is at the front and behind it are the driver (at the left) and commander, who also operates the 12.7-mm machine gun mounted on the hull roof (except in the PW-GWT). Behind them is the main crew compartment, with double access doors in the rear plate of the hull. In the hull roof there is a hatch over the driver and six hatches, not all of the same size, over the rear compartment.

The engine is a DAF DS575 in-line six-cylinder water-cooled turbo supercharged diesel, developing 165 h.p. at 2,400 r.p.m. The transmission is interesting: the five-speed gearbox is immediately behind the engine and is linked to a two-speed transfer box, located on the floor between the driver and the commander. Here the transmission is split into an H pattern, shafts on each side going

forward to the front pair of wheels and rearwards through universal couplings to the four rear wheels. The second pair of wheels is not driven (although, with the front pair, steerable) but provides weight distribution and prevents bellying (in the YA-328 6 × 6 truck a pair of spare wheels in a similar position is also an anti-bellying device, although they are not normally in contact with the ground).

The suspension of the front pair of wheels is on double trailing arms controlled by transverse torsion bars, and the second pair are similarly suspended but use longitudinal torsion bars. The assembly for the four rear wheels is carried on two longitudinal semi-elliptic leaf springs supporting a transverse beam with centrally pivoted balancing beams on which the wheels are mounted. Steel cables limit the movement of the balancing beams. The tyres have reinforced walls which, if punctured, enable the vehicle to be driven at a reduced speed for up to 50 km. The second pair of wheels also act as spares for the others, provision being made for the wheelless axle to be suspended by a chain. The YP-408, which weighs about 12 tons, has a maximum road speed of 80 km/h and a very satisfactory cross-country performance.

It should be mentioned that prototypes for another armoured vehicle, the YP-104, a scout car equivalent to the British Ferret Mark 1, were also built by DAF in 1959–60, but this did not go into production.

DAF YP-408

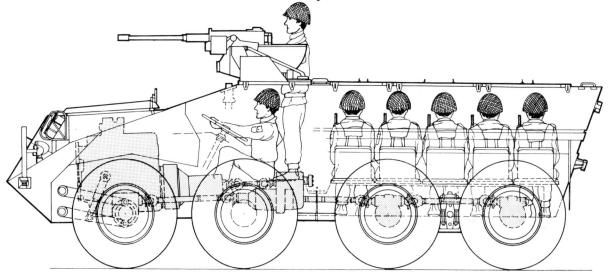

South Africa

Ratel Armoured Personnel Carrier, 6 × 6
Plates 44 and 45

During World War 2 over 5,700 armoured cars of South African design were built in the Union of South Africa, as it then was, and served with Commonwealth forces in several theatres of war. When the time came to replace wartime wheeled armoured vehicles in the South African Defence Forces, British Ferret scout cars and Saracen armoured personnel carriers were purchased (believed to be between 200 and 300 of each). Further supplies of military equipment from the United Kingdom were then prevented by an arms embargo. However the South Africans obtained a licence to manufacture the French Panhard light armoured cars AML H-90 and AML HE 60-7 and over 1,400 of these, known as Eland, are in service. For internal security duties, lightly armoured vehicles such as Hippo, based on standard 4 × 4 truck chassis, have also been built in South Africa to local designs (see Zimbabwe entry).

Fire support version of the Ratel armoured personnel carrier, 6 × 6 armed with a 90-mm gun of French design

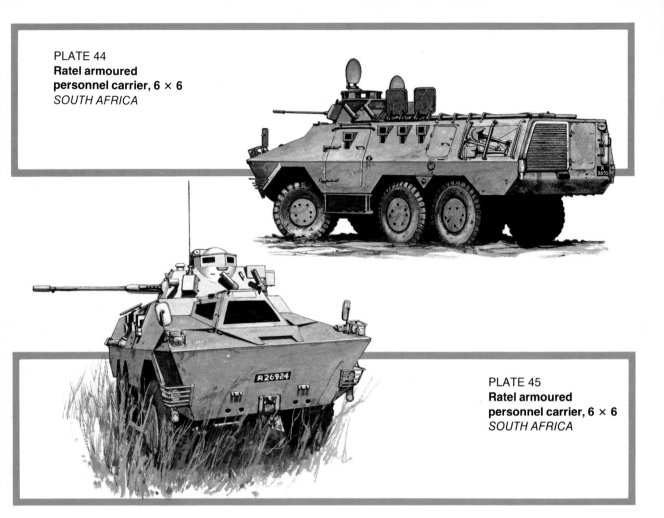

PLATE 44
**Ratel armoured
personnel carrier, 6 × 6**
SOUTH AFRICA

PLATE 45
**Ratel armoured
personnel carrier, 6 × 6**
SOUTH AFRICA

When the need arose to replace older vehicles, particularly the ageing Saracens, in the early 1970s, it appears mainly to have been to France that the South African government looked, and among the vehicles known to have been obtained for test purposes was a Panhard M.6 prototype. This vehicle, named 'Boerboel' in South Africa, was equipped with a 90-mm gun turret like that of the AML H-90, although it was also capable of carrying six troops in the rear compartment in addition to the crew of four.

The decision was taken eventually to design and produce a wheeled armoured vehicle specifically for South African requirements and the result, Ratel (named after the African honey badger), has been in service since 1977. A six-wheeled, six-wheel-drive armoured personnel carrier, the Ratel has a family resemblance to the French four-wheeled Berliet VXB and, apparently, a similar internal layout in that the engine (a six-cylinder diesel with an automatic gearbox) is located at the rear at the left-hand side with access alongside it on the right to a door in the hull back plate.

The infantry compartment for eight is in the centre of the vehicle and there are four firing ports with vision blocks on each side (one each on the side doors) as well as four roof hatches. A two-man turret, immediately behind the driver's cab, is armed with a 20-mm cannon, model F2, of French design, and a coaxial 7.62-mm machine gun, and there are four smoke dischargers, two on each side.

Few performance details have been made available but the Ratel is reported to weigh 16,000 kg, to be capable of a maximum speed of 105 km/h, and able to wade to a depth of 1.2 metres without preparation. A support version of the Ratel, armed with a French-designed 90-mm gun, has followed the standard personnel carrier.

Union of Soviet Socialist Republics

BTR-152 Plates 46 and 47

Developed in the immediate post-war years, the BTR-152 was the Soviet Union's first purpose-built armoured personnel carrier. Produced in large numbers from about 1950 onwards, it is still widely used in many of the African and Asian countries to which it was exported, although it has been withdrawn from front-line service with the Red Army and has also been largely superseded in the armies of most of the Soviet Union's European allies.

The then current ZIS-151 $2\frac{1}{2}$-ton 6×6 truck chassis was used as the basis of the armoured personnel carrier, although the later ZIS-157 chassis was employed for later models of the BTR-152. The all-welded steel hull of the BTR-152 shows traces of both American and German influence in its design — several thousands of

M3A1 4×4 scout cars and M2 and M5 series half-tracks were supplied to the Soviet Union under lend-lease arrangements during World War 2, and many German half-tracks were captured. Like those vehicles, the BTR-152 has a front-mounted engine with, behind, an open-top crew compartment containing the driver, vehicle commander and up to 17 infantrymen (according to model) with their equipment. The driver and commander have separate glass windscreens protected by steel hatches incorporating vision blocks, and each has a side exit door. Access for the infantrymen is via the open roof or through a single door in the rear plate of the hull. There are six firing ports in the hull sides and two in the rear plate either side of the door.

The engine of the BTR-152, the six-cylinder,

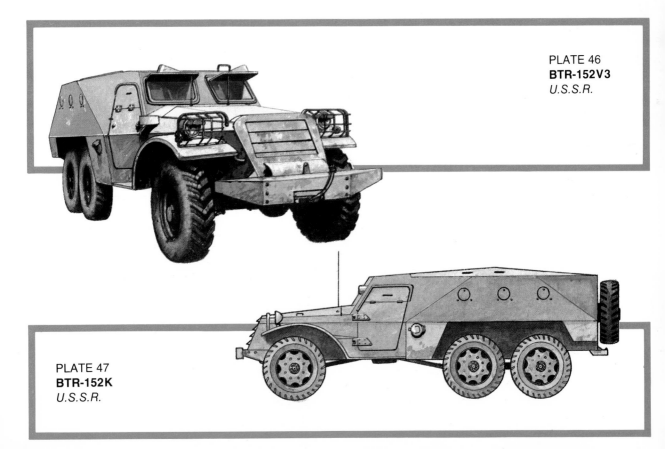

PLATE 46
BTR-152V3
U.S.S.R.

PLATE 47
BTR-152K
U.S.S.R.

in-line model ZIS-123, is a water-cooled petrol type developing 110 h.p. at 2,900 r.p.m. The transmission arrangements are those of a conventional 6 × 6 commercial truck with drive shafts leading to differentials on 'solid' axles. The gearbox has five forward speeds and there is a two-speed transfer box. Most versions of the BTR-152 have a tyre pressure system controlled by the driver to suit varying ground conditions. In some models the air lines leading to the wheel hubs are mounted externally. Another feature present on most, but not all, versions of the BTR-152 is a winch mounted at the front.

Some versions of the BTR-152, intended mainly for signals or command purposes, have roof armour and the BTR-152U is a specialised command vehicle with a much higher, fully enclosed, hull, enabling staff officers to work standing up.

The usual armament is a 7.62-mm machine gun (or, alternatively, a heavy 12.7-mm or 14.5-mm machine gun) mounted on the hull top.

A specialised version of the BTR-152 is the BTR-ZPU, an anti-aircraft vehicle equipped with twin 14.5-mm KPV machine guns in a rotating turret. These guns can also carry armour piercing rounds for use against light armoured vehicles,

the maximum range against ground targets being 2,000 metres, with the capability of penetrating 32 mm of armour at 500 metres. The maximum effective range against aerial targets is 1,400 metres.

BTR-60PB Plates 48 and 49

A heavy eight-wheeled amphibious armoured personnel carrier, the BTR-60P entered service with the Soviet army in 1961. Since then, it has been supplied to well over a dozen different countries in Europe, Asia and Africa and has been built under licence in Romania as the TAB-72.

The BTR-60P series is powered by two GAZ-49B six-cylinder, water-cooled, in-line, petrol engines, developing a total of 180 h.p. These are mounted at the rear of the welded steel hull and drive all eight wheels, the front four of which are steerable. The passenger compartment (originally for 14, but reduced in later models) occupies the centre of the vehicle, and the driver (on the left) and the commander (on the right) are at the front. No overhead protection for the central compartment was provided in the original version, BTR-60P, but the next model, BTR-60PK (later

BTR-152 armoured personnel carrier

known as BTR-60PA) was fully enclosed, with roof hatches provided to supplement access through the two small doors on each side. Armament on the BTR-60P and -60PA usually consisted of either a 12.7-mm or a 7.62-mm machine gun, on a pintle mounting on top of the hull near the front, supplemented by a varying number of 7.62-mm machine guns, also on open mountings.

The final model, the BTR-60PB, is fitted with a small turret on the hull roof near the front, mounting a 14.5-mm machine gun and a 7.62-mm machine gun.

A standard vehicle of the Soviet Naval Infantry as well being used by the army, the BTR-60P series is fully amphibious and is propelled in water by a hydrojet system with a single controllable outlet at the rear. This gives a calm-water speed of 10 km/h, compared with 80 km/h on land. For employment in water a bilge pump is provided, together with a trim vane which is normally carried flat on the nose plate.

Although the BTR-60PB has been built under licence in Romania its major disadvantage, the lack of easy egress for the personnel carried, caused the Czech and Polish governments to develop instead the SKOT series for their armies.

BTR-40 Plates 50 and 51

The BTR-40 is a small armoured personnel carrier-cum-reconnaissance vehicle that was first introduced in 1951 to supplement the earlier and larger BTR-152. In many respects it is a very much improved version of the American M3A scout car, large numbers of which were supplied to the U.S.S.R. during World War 2.

BTR-60PB armoured personnel carrier

BTR-40 armoured personnel carrier

Based on the GAZ-63 truck, although with a shorter wheel-base, the BTR-40 is a conventional four-wheel-drive armoured truck with a front engine layout. It is armoured to an eight-millimetre standard and can carry eight men in addition to the crew of two. The original version was open-topped but was followed by the BTR-40B (earlier known as the BTR-40K) which had an armoured roof with large hatches.

One version of the BTR-40 was adapted as a chemical decontamination vehicle, the equipment of which included a means of placing flag markers to denote contaminated areas. Another version, is the BTR-40A/ZPU. This is an anti-aircraft vehicle mounting twin 14.5-mm KPV heavy machine guns. These weapons, which are in an open turret with 360 degrees traverse, are operated manually and have an effective sustained rate of fire of 150

rounds per minute. They are provided with armour-piercing rounds, as well as anti-aircraft high explosive ammunition, so that they can also be used against light armoured vehicles.

The BTR-40 series is no longer in front line service with the Soviet army or its major European allies, but is still widely used in many other countries where, although lacking an amphibious capability and sophisticated features such as N.B.C. (nuclear, biological and chemical) protection, they continue to give useful service.

BRDM Plates 52 and 53

With an amphibious capability and enhanced cross-country performance, the BRDM, which first appeared in 1959, is the successor to the

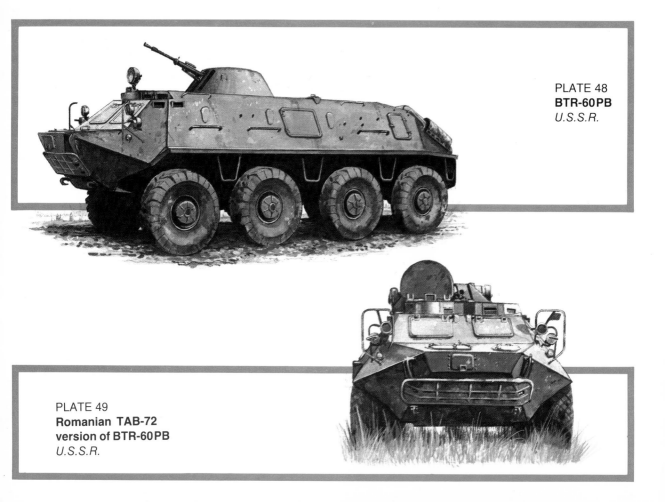

PLATE 48
BTR-60PB
U.S.S.R.

PLATE 49
**Romanian TAB-72
version of BTR-60PB**
U.S.S.R.

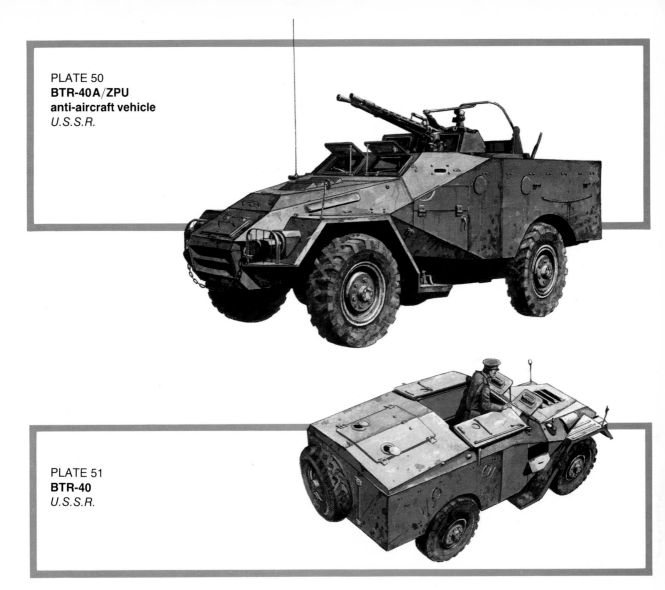

PLATE 50
BTR-40A/ZPU
anti-aircraft vehicle
U.S.S.R.

PLATE 51
BTR-40
U.S.S.R.

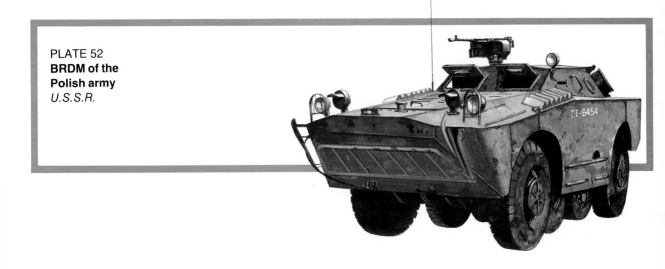

PLATE 52
BRDM of the
Polish army
U.S.S.R.

BTR-40 for reconnaissance purposes. It is a four-wheeled, four-wheel-drive vehicle, but an interesting feature is the four powered auxiliary wheels between the main wheels which can be lowered to both increase the gap-crossing performance and, by increasing the bearing surface, reduce the ground pressure in soft-going to avoid the danger of becoming bogged down.

The BRDM has its engine at the front, mounted with a slight slope to the rear, in line with the four-speed gearbox which is on the floor in the centre of the vehicle. A two-speed transfer box transmits the power through shafts to differentials on the front and rear axles. The power transfer to the four auxiliary wheels is by chain drive. Propulsion in water is by means of a hydrojet system activated by a propeller in a tunnel at the rear of the vehicle. The suspension, front and rear, is on semi-elliptic leaf springs with hydraulic shock absorbers.

The BRDM has a crew of five whose compart-ment comprises approximately the rear half of the vehicle. The driver sits on the left and the commander on the right with the other three crew members behind them. One 7.62-mm machine gun is usually mounted on the hull roof near the front (although sometimes a 12.7-mm machine gun may be substituted) and two firing ports each side of the hull are provided for the crew's personal weapons. There is a large hatch in the roof and two doors in the sloping rear plate of the upper part of the hull. With a loaded weight of 5,600 kg, the BRDM has a top speed of 80 km/h on land and 9 km/h in water.

There are several guided missile derivatives of the BRDM and these are described separately. Although the BRDM has not been as widely distributed as the BTR-40 series and some other Soviet armoured vehicles, it has been supplied to East Germany, Poland and half a dozen or more other countries.

BRDM reconnaissance cars. Although these vehicles are not actually swimming, their trimboards are raised

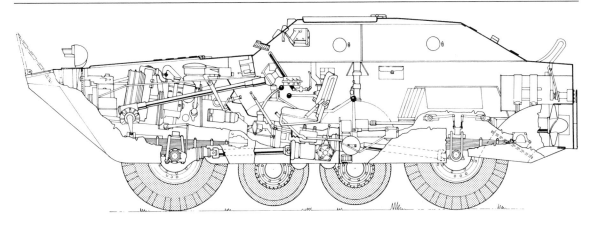

BRDM

BRDM with AT-1 Snapper and AT-2 Swatter Plates 54 and 55

The BRDM reconnaissance car has been adapted as a guided anti-tank missile carrier and has appeared in two versions in this role. The first successful Soviet anti-tank missile was the weapon named AT-1 Snapper by NATO and known in the Warsaw Pact countries as 3M6 Schmel (bumble bee). This wire-guided weapon was originally mounted on a modified GAZ-69 (later known as UAZ-69) $\frac{1}{2}$-ton truck in which the quadruple mounting was completely unarmoured, but on the BRDM it was possible to provide a good measure of protection for a triple mounting of the same weapon. The upper part of the rear hull of the BRDM was extended to accept a retractable launcher for three Snapper missiles which stood clear of the hull top when in action and could be completely covered by sideways-folding plates when not in use. The missile has an effective range of 2,500 metres and can penetrate 380 mm of normal steel armour, but it is wire-guided and

has the disadvantage that the operator has to watch both missile and target throughout the missile's flight. One reload of three missiles is carried inside the vehicle.

A radio-guided missile, known in NATO as AT-2 Swatter, was introduced next and likewise mounted on the BRDM. Although only slightly smaller than Snapper, it was possible to accomodate a retractable quadruple launcher which was fully protected when not in use by folding side and rear plates. Swatter has the same range as Snapper but can penetrate 480 mm of steel armour.

Both Snapper and Swatter were made obsolescent (although not yet fully replaced) by a much better weapon, Malyutka, which was given the NATO name of AT-3 Sagger. Mountings of this kind have been designed for the BRDM-2 as well as the BRDM and are described in more detail separately.

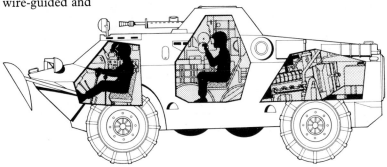

BRDM-2

PLATE 53
BRDM
U.S.S.R.

PLATE 54
BRDM with AT-1 Snapper
U.S.S.R.

PLATE 55
Polish army
BRDM AT-2 Swatter
U.S.S.R.

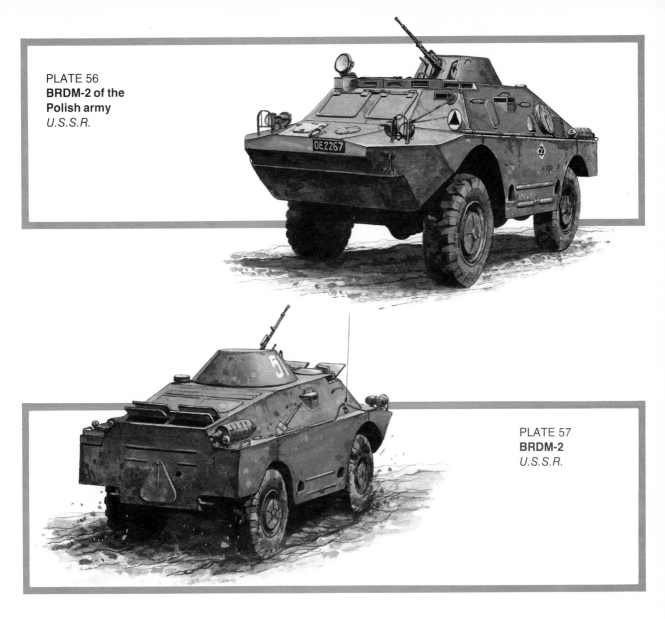

PLATE 56
**BRDM-2 of the
Polish army**
U.S.S.R.

PLATE 57
BRDM-2
U.S.S.R.

BRDM-2 Plates 56 and 57

As a successor to the BRDM, the BRDM-2, which has increased mobility and a small turret but reduced crew capacity and more limited access, appears to be intended more as a purely reconnaissance vehicle than the earlier type. It is fully amphibious, with a similar hydrojet system to the BRDM, but the engine is much more powerful, being a 140-h.p. GAZ-41, V-8 water-cooled petrol unit, and is placed at the rear with the air intakes on top of the rear hull. The four auxiliary wheels of the BRDM, driven by a power take-off from the main engine, are retained in the BRDM-2, maintaining the very high standard of

mobility on both land and water but with increased maximum speeds, compared with the BRDM, of 100 km/h (land) and 10 km/h (water).

The commander and driver occupy seats at the front of the all-welded hull, the driver on the left. Both men are provided with periscopic vision blocks around the front of the top edge of the hull for use when the front hatches protecting the twin windscreens are closed down in action. There is also a group of three vision blocks on each side of the centre of the upper hull. Hatches on the roof of the hull in front of the turret are the only means of entry and exit for the crew, since the turret lacks a hatch.

The armament of the BRDM-2 consists of one 14.5-mm KPVT machine gun and one 7.62-mm machine gun, both mounted in the 360 degrees hand-traversed turret, which is identical to that of the BTR-60PB. There is a guided missile version of the BRDM-2 which is described separately.

Developed some years after the BRDM, the BRDM-2 was first seen in public in 1966. It has been supplied to nearly a dozen different countries including Poland, and a Polish-used vehicle is shown in one of the illustrations.

BRDM-2

BRDM-2 with AT-3 Sagger and BRDM-3 with AT-5 Spandrel Plates 58 and 59

Just as the BRDM was used for the earlier Soviet anti-tank missiles, so the BRDM-2 has been employed as a mounting for the later Malyutka (baby), or AT-3 Sagger as it is known to NATO. This mounting for the launcher for six missiles was also first fitted on the BRDM but has been adapted, with little modification, for the BRDM-2. The whole mount is attached to a single pillar centred over the middle of the vehicle. A single plate over the sextuple launcher provides protection for the equipment and crew when in use and forms the roof of the hull when retracted. The wire-guided missile is much smaller (0.815 metres long compared with 1.14 metres) than Snapper and Swatter but has a far greater range (3,000 metres) and can still penetrate 430 mm of

conventional armour. The reduced size enables a mounting for six missiles to be accommodated, together with eight reserve rounds.

The modifications to the basic BRDM-2, apart from the absence of the turret, include a position for the missile controller to the right of the driver which has a projecting housing for the periscope to control the missiles in flight. This is in place of the normal co-driver's vision hatch.

A new vehicle which is externally almost identical to the BRDM-2 in hull design, although differences in the engine compartment may indicate a new power plant, was first shown in public in 1977. This vehicle, believed to be the BRDM-3, has a new anti-tank missile system provisionally named AT-5 Spandrel in the West and thought to be similar to the Milan missile used by some NATO countries. A wire-guided missile homing on its target by an infra-red heat-seeking system, it has been estimated that the AT-5 can penetrate up to 600 mm of normal steel armour. The launcher for five missiles is mounted in a similar way to AT-3 but lacks the overhead plate and, although it can be traversed, it is not clear if it is retractable. Unlike the AT-3 system on the BRDM-2, the AT-5 carrier vehicle has two normal front vision hatches for the driver and the man on his right.

SA-9 Gaskin on BRDM-2 Plate 60

A mobile anti-aircraft system to accompany armoured and motorised units in the field for protection against low flying aircraft, the SA-9 Gaskin (as it is known to NATO) is carried in a modified version of the BRDM-2 reconnaissance car.

The SA-9 missile is an infra-red heat-homing device developed from the earlier hand-held SA-7 Grail, but with a more powerful solid-fuel rocket motor and a larger warhead. It has a horizontal range of about 6.5 km and vertical range of 4.8 km. The quadruple launcher mounting is on top of a small turret containing the operator behind a window at its base. Out of action, the launcher mounting can be lowered and traversed to the rear to rest on top of the hull deck and side grilles are raised to protect it.

It has been reported that the SA-9 system can be linked with Gun Disk radar as an alternative to the optical sighting system; if so, this equipment is likely to be carried in an accompanying vehicle.

SA-8 Gecko Plate 61

A mobile short-range all-weather anti-aircraft missile system which first appeared in public in 1975 has been given the NATO name of SA-8 Gecko. Carried on a six-wheeled vehicle, it comprises a quadruple launcher, an early warning surveillance and target tracking radar, and two guidance radars all mounted together on one turret. The missile, powered by a solid-fuel rocket, has a range of 19.2 km horizontally or 11.2 km vertically and so can tackle targets outside the range of the SA-9 but below the effective range of the SA-6 Gainful. A feature of the SA-8 Gecko system is its ability to fire a salvo of two missiles at the same target, simultaneously guiding them on different radio frequencies, and so making jamming countermeasures much more difficult.

The Gecko carrier vehicle has six evenly spaced wheels and is not known to have been used for any other equipment, although it is a greatly modified version of the ZIL-167 truck used in Soviet Arctic territories.

SA-8 Geckos on parade in Red Square, Moscow

PLATE 58
**BRDM-3 with AT-5 Spandrel
in parade markings**
U.S.S.R.

PLATE 59
BRDM-2 with AT-3 Sagger
U.S.S.R.

PLATE 60
**Polish army
SA-9 Gaskin on BRDM-2**
U.S.S.R.

PLATE 61
**SA-8 Gecko in
parade markings**
U.S.S.R.

PLATE 62
**FROG-7 with missile
partly elevated**
U.S.S.R.

FROG-7 Plate 62

The latest 'free rocket over ground' (or FROG in NATO terminology) of a series, FROG-7 is carried on a wheeled transporter, unlike the earlier models which employed tracked carriers.

The FROG-7 is a short-range rocket for battlefield support. As its acronym suggests, it is unguided and is used for laying down a barrage of fire on concentrations of infantry or tanks. The maximum range is up to about 70 km and by the use of air brakes on the single-stage rocket the minimum range can be brought down to about 12 km. The launch weight of the missile is about 2,300 kg and high explosive, nuclear and chemical warheads are available, ranging in weight from 390 kg (chemical) to 550 kg (nuclear).

The FROG-7 missile is 9.1 metres long and is carried on an eight-wheeled truck from which it can be launched, a pair of jacks being lowered at the rear of the vehicle and the launching girder elevated for firing. The ZIL-135, used as the launcher-carrier vehicle, is powered by twin ZIL-375 water-cooled petrol engines, each having eight cylinders and developing 180 h.p. at 3,200 r.p.m. The four wheels on one side are driven by one engine and the wheels on the other side are driven by the engine on that side; either engine can keep the vehicle moving in emergency. Only the front and rear pairs of wheels are steerable. A load-carrying version of the ZIL-135 is used as a supply vehicle for FROG batteries and can carry three FROG missiles.

FROG-7

SS-1C Scud B Plate 63

The SS-1C Scud B, as it is known to NATO, a medium range surface-to-surface missile is intended for battlefield support and can attack targets such as stores depots or railway yards some distance behind the combat area. It has a maximum range of about 280 km. The rocket, which is a single-stage missile, uses a liquid propellant and weighs 6,370 kg when ready for launch.

Chemical, high explosive and nuclear warheads are available and weigh between 770 and 860 kg according to type. The missile is 11.4 metres long and can be elevated and fired from the transporter-erector-launcher vehicle.

Tracked carriers were used for Scud A and early Scud Bs, but the current transporter is the eight-wheeled MAZ-543. This vehicle has eight-wheel drive and weighs, with missile, 28 tons. It is powered by a 12-cylinder diesel engine develop-

SS-1C Scud B

ing 375 h.p. at 1,650 r.p.m. The gearbox has three forward and one reverse speeds with a two-speed transfer box, and a maximum speed of 55 km/h can be achieved. The front four wheels, which have torsion bar suspension, are steerable. The crew have a heated, air-conditioned cab which is in two parts (the driver being in the left half), with the nose of the missile lying between them.

Scud B missiles are used by all the Warsaw Pact countries and they have also been exported outside Europe, although nuclear warheads for them are held only by the Soviet Union.

SS-12 Scaleboard Plate 64

Previously known by NATO as SS-1D Scud C, Scaleboard (another NATO name) is, in fact, a very much more powerful missile than Scud and has a range of perhaps 800 km, which brings it nearer to the category of a strategic weapon than that of a battlefield support weapon. More than half of France and much of east and south-east England would come within this range from firing positions in East Germany.

In most other respects, however, the SS-12 and its transporter-erector-launcher vehicle are similar to the SS-1C. The same MAZ-543 chassis is used with a more fully enclosed body behind the cab, and the missile is erected in a similar way although it is contained in a casing which encloses it until it is ready for firing. The missile also uses liquid propellant and has the same range of warheads as Scud.

PLATE 63
SS-1C Scud B
U.S.S.R.

PLATE 64
**SS-12 Scaleboard shown
in parade markings**
U.S.S.R.

United Kingdom

Scout Car, Liaison, Ferret Mark 1 and Scout Car, Recce, Ferret Mark 2
Plates 65 and 66

Two of the most successful British armoured vehicles of World War 2 were not tanks but wheeled vehicles, the Daimler Scout Car and Daimler Armoured Car, of which 6,626 and 2,694 respectively were produced. Both types epitomised the British philosophy that the value of reconnaissance units lay in the quality of the information they relayed to headquarters rather than the amount of direct damage they could inflict on the enemy. Both were compact, fast and manoeuvrable vehicles, the scout car particularly so, being only about five feet (1.5 metres) high with a top speed of 60 m.p.h. (96 km/h).

A second type of British-built scout car, the Humber, was also produced in World War 2, mainly to supplement the Daimlers which were in short supply. The Humber Scout Car's mechanical design was based on that of existing four-wheel-drive vehicles, with 'solid' axles, by the same manufacturer and did not enjoy as good a performance as the Daimler, but was more roomy with seats for three. For these reasons, Humber Scout Cars tended to be used, where possible, at the headquarters of armoured regiments for general liaison purposes, rather than for scouting, when Daimlers were available for that function.

In addition to armoured cars and scout cars, a third type of light wheeled armoured vehicle was used in large numbers by the British Army in World War 2 — the light reconnaissance car. This type had a crew of three and (apart from early improvised vehicles) a turret mounting a Bren light machine gun, and also carried a 0.55-in (14-mm) anti-tank rifle. Most commonly used in reconnaissance regiments of infantry divisions, light reconnaissance cars had some features in common with scout cars, although they lacked the mechanical sophistication of the Daimler vehicles to which they were generally inferior in performance.

In 1947 the War Office issued a specification for a new scout car to replace the many wartime scout cars that were still in service with the British Army. A second specification for an almost identical vehicle, bur fitted with a small turret and

PLATE 65
Scout Car, Recce, Ferret Mk 2
U.K.

PLATE 66
Scout Car, LRV, Ferret Mk 1/2
U.K.

capable of acting as a light reconnaissance car, followed. The first vehicle in its definitive form became FV.701C Fieldmouse, and the second was FV.701E, Ferret. The more aggressive creature's name was soon adopted for both types, however, for which the full designations indicated their respective roles — Car, Scout, 4 × 4, Liaison (Ferret) Mark 1 and Car, Scout, 4 × 4, Reconnaissance (Ferret) Mark 2.

The Daimler Company Limited, which designed the new vehicles, drew heavily on wartime experience with armoured cars and scout cars and employed a mechanical layout very similar to that of the Daimler Scout Cars. With a longer wheelbase, however, three men could be carried, a characteristic that had been found useful in the Humber Scout Cars. One feature of the wartime Daimler Scout Cars that was dropped, however, was the 30-mm front glacis plate. In 1939 this offered good protection against most anti-tank weapons for a scout car leading a column, but the wartime development of both conventional guns and rocket projectors with hollow-charge projectiles meant that adequate protection in a light vehicle against such weapons was entirely impracticable by 1947. Thus, in accordance with the specification, most of the armour was between 12 and 16 mm which is only sufficient protection against machine guns, small arms and shell splinters.

The engine used for the Ferret is one of a series of Rolls-Royce engines developed for military use; the B.60 Mark 6A is an in-line six-cylinder water-cooled petrol engine developing 129 b.h.p. at 3,750 r.p.m. The transmission is via a Daimler fluid coupling clutch and a preselective five-speed gearbox (also of Daimler design) to a transfer box. From the transfer box, four propellor shafts (in the form of an H in plan, the transfer box representing the cross-bar) lead to each wheel where there is a bevel box and hub reduction gears. This system, with the drive shafts at either side of the hull, enables the floor to be lowered and the vehicle's overall height to be less than that of a comparable vehicle with central transmission shafts. The suspension is fully independent, each wheel being mounted on coil springs with a wishbone linkage system. A shock absorber is carried inside each coil spring.

The Ferret Mark 1 is only 1.448 metres to the top of its hull, but, lacking a turret, the only means of self defence is a 7.62-mm machine gun that can be fitted on a pintle mounting and operated by the vehicle commander or third man in the crew.

The Ferret Mark 2, with an overall height of 1.879 metres, is more conspicuous than the Mark 1, but its turret gives it a more efficient means of self protection at the expense of reducing the crew to two. The turret, armed with a 7.62-mm Browning machine gun mounted on the right-hand side, was originally identical to that of the Saracen armoured personnel carrier and had an inside ring diameter of 710 mm. This was felt to be too small, however, and a wider turret on a 760-mm ring, with more headroom, replaced it.

During its long production run, which ended in 1971 when 4,409 had been built and were in service in nearly 40 countries throughout the world, various minor improvements were introduced as well as some variants of the two basic models. One of the more distinctive of the latter is the Ferret Mark 1/2, the Scout Car, LRV (FV.704). This has a flat multi-sided armoured structure added on top of the centre part of the hull, increasing the vehicle's height, compared with the Mark 1, to 1.651 metres. Extra vision slits are provided in the sides and rear of the superstructure, and two periscopes at the front for the vehicle commander. There is a pintle mounting for a light machine gun. By providing observation facilities under full armoured protection, with a three-man crew, this model of the Ferret was intended specifically as a light liaison and reconnaissance vehicle for the infantry, although it has also proved to be a suitable command or reconnaissance vehicle at troop commander's level in artillery units.

The final version of the ordinary Ferret Mark 1 was FV.701J or Ferret Mark 1/1. This incorporated various minor changes. A modification to the Ferret Mark 2 by the British Army overseas, and employed in such places as Aden and Malaya, was designated Ferret Mark 2/2 (FV.701G). This version, not produced in great numbers, had the turret raised on a multi-sided armoured box, following the lines of the hull. While improving observation in internal security operations, increasing the overall height by about 0.2 metres reduced somewhat the Ferret's general usefulness as a reconnaissance vehicle.

The Ferret Mark 2/3 (FV.701H) is the basic turreted version updated with minor improvements. It can be fitted with ZB 298 ground surveillance radar. Ferrets Mark 2/4 (FV.701K) and Mark 2/5 (FV.701L) have additional armour.

The addition of Vigilant wire-guided anti-tank weapons to a Ferret Mark 2 resulted in the Scout Car, Recce/GW, Ferret Mark 2/6 (FV.703) and a reconnaissance vehicle capable, if necessary, of defeating heavy tanks — a concept far removed from the passive role of the original Ferret Mark 1. The missiles in their launcher boxes are carried one each side of the turret, with two spares in their boxes on the left side of the hull. The Ferret Mark 2/6 with the guided weapon installation removed is known as the Mark 2/7.

Further basic developments of the Ferret series introduced larger wheels and full floatation capability and are described separately. One unusual field modification of the Ferret Mark 2 was as an improvised mineclearer used in Cyprus in 1959. This had two pairs of caster wheels attached to weighted girders pushed in front of the Ferret in line with its wheel track.

The Ferret weighs between 4,210 kg (Mark 1) and 4,560 kg (Mark 2/6) but the maximum speed in both cases is 93 km/h.

Scout Car, Recce 0.30-in M.G., Ferret Mark 4 (FV.711) and Scout Car, Recce/GW 7.62-mm M.G., Ferret Mark 5 (FV.712) Plates 67 and 68

Although the Ferret in its original versions was in most respects a highly satisfactory vehicle, it was felt necessary to improve the cross-country performance and provide an inherent swimming capability.

Early water-crossing experiments with the Ferret included fitting a collapsible screen (like those of wartime D.D. tanks) to the top of the hull of a Ferret Mark 1 which, with a sealed hull and engine compartment, could then wade to a depth of 1.5 metres compared with 0.9 metres for a standard vehicle. A Ferret Mark 2/3 was then made fully amphibious by adding three large inflatable rubberised fabric buoyancy bags, one at the front and one at each side. Neither of these experimental vehicles was felt worth putting into production, the first because the apparatus needed to merely increase the wading ability was out of proportion to the result achieved, and the second because the equipment, which was clumsy, only enabled the Ferret to float and it normally had to be towed when in water.

An inherently amphibious Ferret was achieved when a Mark 1 had its hull enlarged with rigid polyeurethane foam sections covered with a skin of glass-fibre reinforced plastic. With vertical panels increasing the freeboard of the engine compartment, this version could both float and, as it had a reasonably streamlined hull form, be propelled in water by its wheels.

The final step in achieving full amphibious capability was to redesign the hull to incorporate built-in reinforced plastic stowage boxes (to increase buoyancy) and a collapsible floatation screen around its top edge. Half a dozen Ferret Mark 1/1s were successfully converted in this way, but further development and production of a fully amphibious Ferret was concentrated on the improved models characterised mainly by larger wheels, Ferret Marks 3 and 4. Design work on the Mark 3, which would have been the improved version of the turretless Ferret Mark 1 series, did not, in fact, go beyond the drawing board and so the Ferret Mark 4, with a turret, became the first of the improved Ferret series.

The changes introduced in the Ferret Mark 4 were not revolutionary but the employment of larger tyres, 11.00×20 in place of the 9.00×16 size, and a wider track improved cross-country performance on land and buoyancy in water. The amphibious system with the floatation screen tested on Mark 1 Ferrets was adopted, and stopping power was improved by the use of disc instead of drum brakes. The suspension was strengthened at the same time. The Scout Car, Recce 0.30-in. M.G., Ferret Mark 4 (FV.711) was followed by a guided-weapon version that was mechanically the same and had a similar hull, but was equipped with a new turret. This vehicle, FV.712, is the Scout Car, Recce/GW 7.62-mm M.G., Ferret Mark 5. The turret, of welded aluminium construction, represents the first use

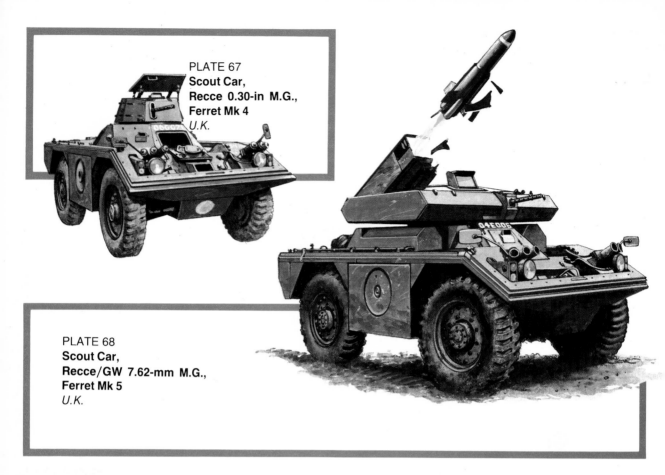

PLATE 67
**Scout Car,
Recce 0.30-in M.G.,
Ferret Mk 4**
U.K.

PLATE 68
**Scout Car,
Recce/GW 7.62-mm M.G.,
Ferret Mk 5**
U.K.

of aluminium armour in a British A.F.V., leading to its wider use in the wheeled and tracked Combat Vehicle Reconnaissance (CVR) series of vehicles. Extending to almost the full hull width, the turret, on an 810-mm ring, carries four Swingfire missiles in their launching boxes, two on each side. The missiles have to be elevated for firing but are otherwise ready for use. Two spare missiles are carried on the hull under armour. A 7.62-mm machine gun is mounted in the centre of the turret face. The Swingfire wire-guided missile cannot be used against targets at under 150 metres but has a maximum range of 4,000 metres and its shaped-charge warhead can penetrate heavy armour. It can, if necessary, be controlled from outside the vehicle at some distance by a cable link with a separate sighting and control unit.

The Ferret Mark 5 was intended to replace the Ferret Mark 2/6 in British armoured car regiments and give them a greatly increased anti-tank capability but, in fact, only about 50 were produced before a change in British Army policy

resulted in the tracked Striker CVR(T) being used for this role. Nevertheless, mechanically (as well as in the introduction of aluminium armour) the Ferret Mark 5 was an interim stage between the original Ferret and the Fox, the first of the CVR series to be built.

Both the Ferret Mark 4 and Mark 5 are only slightly longer and wider than the earlier models, but height (2.336 metres and 2.044 metres respectively) and weight (5,400 kg and 5,890 kg) are more noticeably increased. Although the cross-country performance is better, thanks to the improved suspension, the maximum speed is reduced to 80 km/h.

Combat Vehicle, Reconnaissance, Wheeled, 30-mm Gun, Fox (FV.721)
Plates 69 and 70

The world's first armoured car with all-aluminium armour, the Fox is a development of the Ferret, many of whose features it shares. With the same wheelbase and track dimensions as the

PLATE 69
**Combat Vehicle, Recce,
Wheeled, 30-mm Gun, Fox**
U.K.

PLATE 70
**One of the prototypes
of Combat Vehicle, Recce,
Wheeled, 30-mm Gun, Fox,
which differs in
detail from production
vehicle (Plate 69)**
U.K.

Ferret Scout Cars, Marks 4 and 5, the general arrangement of the crew and engine compartments of the Fox is similar and the same form of transmission and suspension is used for both types. However, the more powerful Jaguar engine, developing 195 b.h.p. at 4,750 r.p.m., gives the Fox a much higher power/weight ratio and a maximum speed of 100 km/h. The Jaguar XK six-cylinder water-cooled engine is also common to the tracked vehicles of the CVR series. Apart from the engine, the main automotive innovation in the Fox is the introduction of powered steering.

The hull and turret of the Fox are made mainly of welded aluminium plates. Being thicker than steel armour, to give the same degree of protection, the alloy armour is therefore more rigid. This enables some of the stiffeners needed with steel armour to be dispensed with, making the alloy-armoured vehicle lighter and also rather less obstructed internally.

A 30-mm Rarden gun and a 7.62-mm machine gun are mounted coaxially in the two-man turret,

in which the commander (who also acts as loader) is on the left and the gunner on the right. The commander's vision arrangements when the vehicle is closed down consist of seven periscopes on the turret roof around his hatch and a binocular periscope in a rotating mounting capable of ×10 or ×1 magnification. The gunner also has a binocular ×10 and ×1 magnification periscope linked to the guns for sighting, two normal periscopes and an image intensifier night sighting device.

Developed by the Royal Armament Research and Development Establishment and the Enfield Royal Small Arms Factory, from which its name

Combat Vehicle, Reconnaissance, Wheeled, 30-mm Gun, Fox

is derived, the Rarden gun's armour-piercing discarding sabot (A.P.D.S.) projectiles can penetrate most armour except the frontal protection of battle tanks. The A.P.D.S. round has a muzzle velocity of 1,200 m/s and the gun has a maximum rate of fire of up to 100 rounds per minute. Single shots or bursts of up to six rounds would be normal, however. Ninety-three rounds of 30-mm ammunition are carried, including high explosive as well as armour-piercing projectiles. As the Rarden gun can be elevated to 40 degrees, it can be used against helicopters and low flying aircraft as well as ground targets. The coaxial 7.62-mm machine gun on the left of the Rarden gun has 2,600 rounds, and the Fox's armament is completed by two three-barrelled smoke dischargers (one group each side of the turret face) for which 12 smoke grenades are carried, six of them stowed in reserve.

The Fox is able to wade to a depth of 1.01 metres without preparation and swim with the use of a collapsible fabric screen that can be erected by the crew in little over a minute. The screen has transparent panels at the front for the driver's benefit; when folded it is carried stowed around the top edge of the hull. It is not fitted in operational areas where it is unlikely to be needed. Propulsion and steering in water is by means of the road wheels, and a maximum speed of about 5.5 km/h can be attained. The Fox is readily air-portable and can be dropped by parachute.

The development of the Fox was carried out by Daimler Ltd of Coventry, a firm that, with its Lanchester subsidiary, had supplied armoured cars in quantity to the British forces since 1915, including the highly successful Daimler Scout Cars and Armoured Cars of World War 2. The production contract for the Fox was, however, given to the Royal Ordnance Factory in Leeds, although links in the production field with the British motor car industry are maintained through Alvis Ltd (a BL subsidiary) at Coventry, which supply the turrets and, of course, Jaguar Cars Ltd which provide the engines.

The Fox, while derived from the Ferret Scout Car, is really the successor in the British Army to the much heavier Saladin 6 × 6 armoured car, although some tactical rethinking on reconnaissance vehicles had taken place by the mid-1960s when design commenced. A direct functional successor to the Ferret was proposed as part of the CVR(W) series in a parallel design to the Fox, and known as Vixen, or CVR(W) Liaison (FV.722). This vehicle, several prototypes of which were produced by the Royal Ordnance Factory, Leeds, in 1971, had the same engine and automotive components as the Fox but a redesigned hull enabled four men to be carried. The armament consisted of one 7.62-mm machine gun in a small turret that also had two four-barrelled smoke dischargers. Although it had a better performance than Ferret, the Vixen was both less inconspicuous and considerably heavier, and its advantages over the earlier vehicle were not sufficient to prevent its further development being terminated as a result of the British Defence expenditure cuts in 1974. The Fox, on the other hand, has been produced for the British Army and for several African and Asian countries.

A new version of Fox, primarily intended for export markets, appeared in 1980. Known as Panga, it has a new turret armed with a 12.7-mm machine gun, or alternatively with one or two 7.62-mm machine guns or one 12.7-mm and one 7.62-mm machine guns.

Fox

Armoured Car, 76-mm Gun, Saladin Mark 2 (FV.601C) Plates 71 and 72

The Saladin armoured car grew out of the need of the British Army to replace wartime armoured cars. The best of these was the Daimler Armoured Car in its Mark 2 version, but this was armed with only a two-pounder (40-mm) gun and a 7.92-mm machine gun, and so by the end of World War 2 armoured car squadrons usually included a support troop of heavy armoured cars armed with 75-mm guns. A four-man crew (although not made an essential qualification) and an improvement over the Daimler's performance were desired without a material increase in its dimensions, armour thickness or size of armament. The

last requirement did not mean that a higher penetrative performance was not necessary, but that the gun's dimensions should be kept within a reasonable size. A better cross-country performance inevitably meant changing to a multi-wheeled layout, so the specification, despite its qualifying clauses, was asking rather a lot. For the record, the Daimler Mark 2 Armoured Car's hull was 3.96 metres long (excluding the gun), 2.44 metres wide, and 2.24 metres to the top of the turret. The FV.601C finally emerged with corresponding dimensions of 4.93 metres long, 2.54 metres wide and 2.39 metres high.

The wartime German eight-wheeled cars (SdKfz 231 and 234 series) were also taken into consideration, and while their off-the-road per-

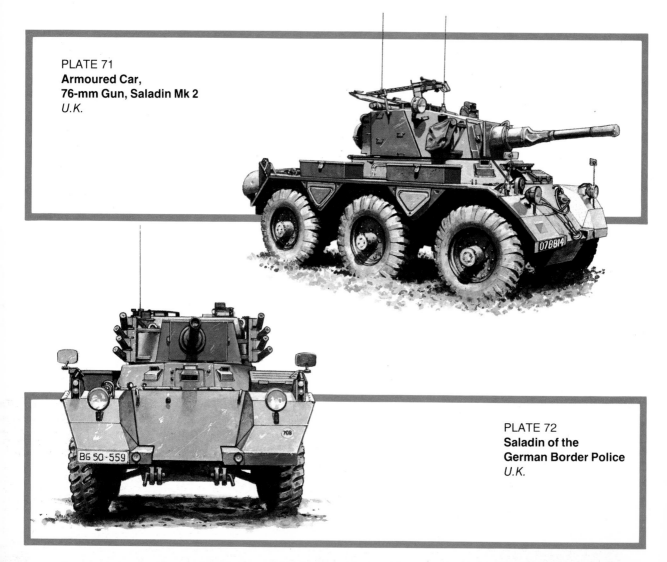

PLATE 71
Armoured Car,
76-mm Gun, Saladin Mk 2
U.K.

PLATE 72
Saladin of the
German Border Police
U.K.

formance was excellent, their bulk was felt by the British to be a severe disadvantage in a reconnaissance vehicle. Consequently it was decided to use symmetrical six-wheeled layout, similar to that chosen by the Americans for their M38 built by the Chevrolet Division of the General Motors Corporation.

Two prototypes to specification FV.601 for the new armoured car were ordered from Alvis Ltd of Coventry in October 1947. This firm had earlier experience with armoured cars and light tanks of advanced concept designed by Nicholas Straussler in the years immediately before World War 2. It is worth recording that Nicholas Straussler, who severed his connection with Alvis in 1938 but continued his active interest in A.F.V.s throughout the War, designed a 12-ton six-wheeled amphibious armoured car about 1949. This was similar in appearance to what became Saladin, although it did not get beyond the drawing board.

A mock-up of the FV.601A, the armoured car with a new version of the two-pounder gun known as Pipsqueak, was produced. This gun had a muzzle velocity of 1,295 m/s, with armour-piercing discarding sabot (A.P.D.S.) ammunition, capable of penetrating 85-mm armour at an angle of 30 degrees from a range of 900 metres. However, it was then decided that the high explosive two-pounder round was inadequate, a

fact that had been well known during the war. Another gun, necessarily of higher calibre, was needed and it was decided to use a new design of 76-mm gun not yet fully developed and tested. The employment of this larger gun meant that a crew of four was no longer possible and the duties of the crew were rearranged for three men. The rear emergency driving controls, present in the Daimler Armoured Cars and originally specified for the FV.601, were also removed at this time in order to allow more ammunition to be stowed for the bigger gun and to give better access to the engine compartment.

The two prototype vehicles were completed by the end of 1952 and early 1953 and used for running trials. Alvis Ltd, in the meantime, had had to give priority to the design and production of the Saracen armoured personnel carrier because of the urgent need for this kind of vehicle in Malaya. Accordingly the contract for six preproduction vehicles of the modified design of the car with the 76-mm gun, FV.601B, was given to Crossley Motors Ltd, Stockport, another firm with a history of building armoured cars between the two World Wars. It was apparently intended that Crossley should become the 'production parents' for the eventual production run, although this, in fact, reverted to Alvis.

The six preproduction vehicles were ready by

Armoured Car, 76-mm Gun, Saladin Mk 2

1954 and were designated Armoured Car, 6 × 6 (Saladin) Mark 1 (FV.601B). Despite the full Service title, further improvements were made before the series production run started. These included a changed shape for the rear of the turret and revised roof hatches (the turret crew roles had been changed from commander/gunner and loader/radio operator, as earlier envisaged, to commander/loader and radio operator/gunner), a modified gun sighting, and disc brakes instead of drum brakes. Even after the appearance of the first Armoured Car 6 × 6 (Saladin) Mark 2 (FV.601C), as it was originally designated, a few further changes took place. Elimination of the gun barrel counterbalance weight at the muzzle, and the replacement of a large ring for the 0.30-in anti-aircraft machine gun (a 0.50-in Browning of the kind so often discarded on American tanks in British use in World War 2 was originally proposed) by a simpler mounting were the most obvious modifications, although there were also improvements in hull and turret protection.

Production of the Saladin took place from 1958 until 1972, when they had been supplied to the British Army and the forces of 17 different countries. Most of these were basically standard vehicles, except for those provided for the German Border Police who had a redesigned gun mantlet, as the coaxial machine gun was not required, and German pattern lighting and multiple smoke dischargers.

The Saladin is both heavier and larger than the Daimler Armoured Car which it was primarily intended to replace. However, it is at the same time over one ton lighter and also smaller than the four-wheeled wartime A.E.C. heavy armoured car that offered a closer comparison with Saladin in armament and protection but not mobility. The Saladin's engine is the Rolls-Royce B.80 Mark 6, a water-cooled, eight-cylinder, in-line, petrol model developing 160 b.h.p. at 3,750 r.p.m. This is mounted at the rear and separated from the crew compartment by a fireproof bulkhead. The transmission layout is similar to that used in the wartime Daimler Armoured and Scout Cars (and continued in the Ferret and its successors), namely a central transfer box from which drive shafts parallel with the inner sides of the hull lead forward and back to the individual wheel stations

where there are hub reduction gears. Splitting the transmission in this way enables the floor of the crew area to be lower than a central transmission system would allow and hence reduces the overall height for the vehicle. A Daimler fluid coupling is used and the five-speed epicyclic preselective gearbox is also of Daimler design. The suspension is of the torsion bar type with hydraulic shock absorbers and is independent for each wheel. The steering operates on the front four wheels and is power-assisted.

The Saladin's wheel arrangement and suspension give it a good cross-country performance. Its manufacturers were perhaps the first to publicise the point that the Saladin (and this applies to other multi-wheeled vehicles) is less likely to be immobilised by mine damage than many tracked vehicles because up to two wheels can be put out of action (provided that both are not on the same side and one front wheel is left intact) without stopping the vehicle.

The combined driver's and fighting compartment is eight-sided in plan. The driver is at the front, immediately behind the glacis plate and has a steering wheel sloping towards him, a useful space saving device. The fighting compartment behind the driver is surmounted by the turret in which the commander at the right also acts as loader and the gunner is at the left. The gunner is also the radio operator, the radio equipment (a C13 and a B.47 transceiver) being carried inside the rear overhang of the turret.

The gun is the 76-mm weapon specially developed for the Saladin by the Armament Development Establishment (later R.A.R.D.E.) and is known as L5A1. A total of 42 rounds is carried, stowed around the sides and rear of the fighting compartment, and these normally include H.E.S.H. (high explosive squashhead, with a muzzle velocity of 533 m/s), high explosive, canister, and smoke. A 7.62-mm Browning machine gun is mounted on the left of and coaxially with the 76-mm gun. A similar Browning machine gun is mounted over the commander's hatch. A total of 12 smoke grenade dischargers is mounted on the turret front, six either side. Both the hull and turret of the Saladin are constructed of all-welded steel plate, varying from 32 mm at a 15-degree slope on the turret front to

10 mm on the hull and turret roofs.

Although the Saladin has largely been replaced in the British Army by Fox, an armoured car only just over half its weight, and by light tracked vehicles, it nevertheless continues to provide useful service in many countries throughout the world.

Carrier, Personnel, Wheeled, A.P.C., Saracen Mark 2 (FV.603B)
Plates 73 and 74

Armoured personnel carriers in the British Army at the end of World War 2 were nearly all American or Canadian in origin and ranged from turretless tanks, through half-tracks, to armoured 15-cwt ($\frac{3}{4}$-ton) trucks. A range of high-mobility wheeled vehicles, commencing with the FV.601 armoured car (later named Saladin), was planned to meet the post-war needs of the British Army. Development of an armoured personnel carrier to the specification FV.603 was, however, brought forward well in advance of the armoured car (an armoured command vehicle design FV.602 having been abandoned at an early stage) because the British Army's operations in Malaya (now Malaysia) demonstrated the urgent need for a modern fully-enclosed armoured vehicle of this kind. This urgency resulted in the first prototype FV.603 being ready in 1950, the design and production 'parents' being Alvis Ltd of Coventry. The preproduction batch were known as FV.603A, or Saracen Mark 1, and these were used for trials while the main production version, Saracen Mark 2 (FV.603B) was already on the assembly lines. The differences between the Marks 1 and 2 were not, in fact, very great although there were some early problems with both suspension and cooling. The Mark 2 eventually emerged with a Rolls-Royce B.80 Mark 6A engine instead of the B.80 Mark 3A of the earlier vehicles, changes in screw thread standards, and (the main external difference) a downward-hinged door at the back of the turret instead of two smaller outward-opening doors.

The Saracen, as a member of the FV.600 family, uses a similar suspension system and the same engine as the Saladin armoured car and, in fact, nearly half of all the automotive parts are common to both the A.P.C. and the armoured car. As unobstructed rear doors for entry and exit from the personnel carrier were necessary, it was decided to place the Saracen's engine at the front, and thus the drive train is in the reverse order to that of the rear-engined Saladin.

Behind the engine compartment is the crew compartment in which the driver's seat is at the front in the centre. Immediately behind the driver is the vehicle commander's seat, which is raised to enable him to observe from the turret top or to operate the 7.62-mm Browning machine gun, for which a periscopic sight is provided. Either side of the vehicle commander's seat are two forward-facing seats, that on the left normally occupied by the infantry section commander, and that on the right by the radio operator. Eight seats, four on each side facing inwards, are provided for infantrymen. Although designed before the concept of a mechanised infantry combat vehicle, the Saracen has a total of eight ports from which small arms can be operated (three each side and two in the rear doors) as well as a hatch in the roof near the rear from which a machine gun on a ring mounting can be used against air or ground targets. The machine gun is either the normal British infantry 7.62-mm General Purpose Machine Gun (G.P.M.G.) or a Browning machine gun similar to that mounted in the turret. Apart from the large sideways-opening rear doors, emergency exit doors are provided in each side of the hull over the centre pair of wheels. The driver's downward-opening hatch is also large enough to serve as an emergency exit.

Carrier, Personnel, Wheeled, A.P.C., Saracen Mk 2

PLATE 73
**Carrier Personnel,
Wheeled A.P.C., Saracen Mk 2**
U.K.

PLATE 74
**Ambulance version
of Saracen Mk 2 used
in Northern Ireland**
U.K.

Further automotive development of the Saladin after the Mark 2 lay mainly in the introduction of reverse flow cooling for vehicles used in very hot countries. The normal engine cooling arrangements caused discomfort to the driver in extreme ambient heat through overheating the engine bulkhead, so arrangements were made instead for the air to be drawn in just in front of the bulk head and expelled forwards over the engine.

The principal functional derivatives of the basic armoured personnel carrier have been command vehicles of different kinds. The FV.604 is externally similar to the armoured personnel carrier, although some vehicles have the turret removed. To adapt it as a regimental command vehicle, carrying three staff officers and two radio operators in addition to the driver, extra radios, desks and stowage bins are installed, and there is an external generator and other minor changes outside. The FV.610 was designed originally as an artillery command vehicle but has been used also by formation commanders in the British Army. The hull has been widened and the height raised from the two metres of the FV.604 to 2.362 metres, enabling the staff officers to work in a standing position. There are a number of variants of FV.610, according to whether it is used by the guns position officer (G.P.O.), command post officer, unit adjutant, etc.; all have additional radios, according to their role, and the extra generator capacity needed for their prolonged operation, as well as the various impedimenta required by regimental or formation headquarters staff, such as fixed and folding tables, map hanging space and adequate internal lighting. Like the FV.604, extra covered working space can be provided, when in the static role, by tent extensions that can be added at either side and the rear. In the artillery command role the FV.610 can be fitted with the field artillery computer system FACE.

The FV.611 is a specialised ambulance adaptation of the raised-hull FV.160 which is fitted to carry either three stretchers and two seated patients, two stretchers and six seated patients, or ten seated patients. In each case the crew consists of the driver and a medical orderly. However, standard Saracens can be and have been used as ambulances with relatively slight modifications.

Two Saracen modifications for particular functions were the Carrier, Mine Exploder, Wheeled version intended for use in Aden, in which heavy tank road wheels were pushed ahead of the vehicle to detonate mines, and a water-gun-equipped vehicle, primarily for use in Northern Ireland. The latter is known as Carrier, Internal Security, Wheeled, Water Gun, Saracen Mark 6.

Because of its long employment in the British Army, Saracen has appeared in at least nine marks, although nearly all are variants and sub-

variants of the mechanical and functional types described above.

Although superseded in the British Army by tracked vehicles for the standard personnel-carrying role, Saracens remain in use for specialised duties and in Northern Ireland where extra protection in the form of grilles and/or wire netting is fitted. The armies and security forces of several African and Asian countries still use the Saracen.

In conclusion, mention should be made of two further members of the FV.600 family — the FV.620 Stalwart, an amphibious load carrier with a 220-h.p. Rolls Royce B.81 engine, used by the British Army, and the FV.652 Salamander aircraft firecrash tender with a 'sprint' version of the same engine to enable it to reach crashed aircraft at high speed across all types of terrain.

Truck, Armoured, 1-ton, 4 × 4, Humber ('Pig') Plates 75 and 76

A new 1-ton load carrier with a high cross-country performance was developed for the British Army

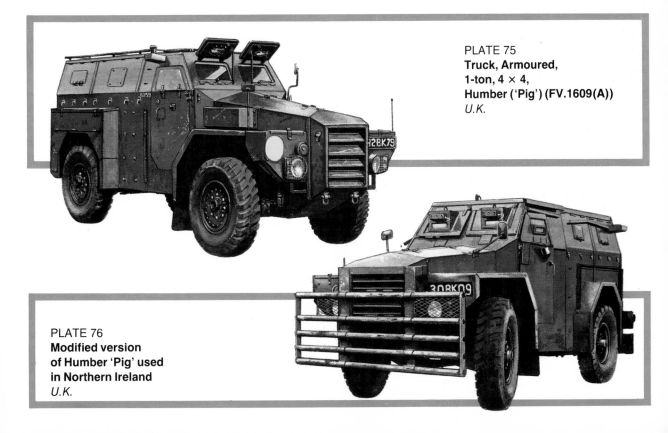

PLATE 75
Truck, Armoured, 1-ton, 4 × 4, Humber ('Pig') (FV.1609(A))
U.K.

PLATE 76
Modified version of Humber 'Pig' used in Northern Ireland
U.K.

by Humber Ltd in the early 1950s. This truck was intended for front line use to replace vehicles in the same class and used what was basically a commercial chassis converted to four-wheel drive with one of the Rolls-Royce standard range of engines, and torsion bar suspension. An armoured version, FV.1609(A) appeared in 1956 and was used on active service in Cyprus and Malaya to supplement Saracen 6 × 6 armoured personnel carriers. The FV.1609(A) had an open top rear compartment but a later version, the FV.1611(A) is fully enclosed. The FV.1612(A) is similar to FV.1611(A) but is fitted with radio, and the FV.1613(A) Ambulance, 3-stretcher, Armoured, 4 × 4 Humber can, as its designation implies, carry three stretcher cases, or one stretcher and four sitting patients, or eight sitting patients.

The Humber 1-ton armoured vehicle has a front engine layout with the driver (at the left) and commander immediately behind the engine and up to eight men (or a radio operator and radio equipment in the FV.1612(A)) behind them. The all-welded hull has front vision hatches for the driver and commander (and both also have circular roof hatches), two side doors incorporating large drop-down hatches, two firing ports on each side, and two doors at the rear which were later modified as described below.

The six-cylinder petrol engine (Rolls-Royce B.60 Mk.5A) producing 120 h.p. at 3,750 r.p.m. gives a maximum speed of about 60 km/h. The gearbox has five speeds and the suspension is of the torsion bar type with hydraulic shock absorbers.

Most of these vehicles were disposed of by the British Army following the introduction of the FV.432 series of tracked armoured personnel carriers. However, the troubles in Northern Ireland resulted in a pressing demand for wheeled armoured personnel carriers and the Humber 1-ton armoured trucks (of the FV.1611, 1612 and 1613 series) were brought back into service. Some had to be repurchased, but eventually 500 were made available for use and, known colloquially as 'Pigs', they have given useful service. By the end of 1971, however, the Irish Republican Army had acquired some armour-piercing ammunition which could pierce the Humber's armour at close

range. Accordingly, all the 'Pigs' were brought back to England in batches between 1972 and 1973 to have their armour increased. The additional weight of about 1.75 tons made it necessary to strengthen the rear axles. At the same time other improvements were made to increase the vehicle's efficiency in urban anti-guerilla operations. The two sideways-opening rear doors were cut down and their upper parts replaced by a full-width upward-opening flap through which the crew could use their weapons and enjoy good vision without opening the doors. An armoured flap was added below the rear doors to protect the legs of soldiers on the ground sheltering behind the vehicle; improvements were also made to the side hatches, and laminated bullet-proof glass blocks were added to all the vision ports. A subsequent addition to some vehicles has been a steel grid attached to the front for pushing aside obstacles. Returned to Northern Ireland, the Humber 'Pigs' have continued, despite their age, to give good service.

Shorland Armoured Patrol Car
Plates 77 and 78

Based on the widely-used Land Rover chassis, the Shorland Armoured Patrol Car was developed by the Royal Ulster Constabulary in Northern Ireland as an armoured vehicle for employment in internal security duties. Using one of their own long wheelbase Series II Land Rovers, the Royal Ulster Constabulary arranged for a mock armoured body of mild steel to be fitted in Belfast, the design of which was suggested by police experience in internal security operations. A flat, square turret was used when the vehicle was completed early in 1963 but, with the cooperation of the British Army, a Ferret Scout Car turret was obtained and substituted. The Rover Company in England was asked to comment on the vehicle, and some mechanical and other changes were made as a result.

The Royal Ulster Constabulary had come to the conclusion, after looking at the prototype, that protection should be improved by sloping the upper parts of the hull sides; with this modification and further changes suggested by experience with the experimental models, together with the special tyres (9.00 × 16 instead of the normal 7.50 × 16) recommended by the Rover Company, the final design (known to the R.U.C. as Mark 3) was approved for production. This commenced at the Belfast works of Short Brothers and Harland Ltd in July 1965, the basic Land Rover components being supplied by the Rover Company Ltd. The name Shorland was adopted, being a combination of Short Brothers and Land Rover.

Ten Shorlands were initially ordered for the R.U.C. but others were supplied to a number of foreign countries at a quite early stage of production. The Shorland is, in fact, an attractive light armoured vehicle from several points of view; its main features are its simplicity of operation and maintenance, arising from its close relationship to the standard Land Rover which is already widely distributed and used all over the world. Initial cost and maintenance costs are relatively low, being only about a quarter of that of a Ferret Scout Car, and the Shorland is even more effective for internal security operations where the Ferret's better cross-country performance is not vital. The sales potential for the Shorland was estimated at 1,000 vehicles and this target seems likely to be

reached, with sales to well over 20 countries already having been achieved.

The Shorlands issued to the Royal Ulster Constabulary were withdrawn in 1969 because of political decisions but were issued to the newly-formed Ulster Defence Regiment of the British Army in Northern Ireland in 1971. In the British Army the Shorlands are known as Truck, Armoured Patrol, 1-ton, 4 × 4, Mark 1 Shorland and Truck Armoured Patrol, 1-ton, 4 × 4, Mark 3 Shorland. Confusingly, different nomenclature from that used by the R.U.C. was adopted by the manufacturers when the Shorland went into production, Mark 1 being the first production model with the four-cylinder Rover petrol engine developing 67 h.p. at 4,100 r.p.m. The Mark 2 (not, apparently, issued to the British Army) has a 77-h.p. engine and the Mark 3 a six-cylinder Rover petrol engine developing 91 b.h.p. at 4,500 r.p.m. The Mark 3 also has extra armour protection.

The general layout of the Shorland, because of its Land Rover derivation, is more like that of a pre-World War 2 armoured car rather than a modern rear-engined armoured car. The normal

Shorland SB.401–armoured personnel carrier version of Shorland armoured patrol car

PLATE 77
**Shorland Mk 3 fitted with
Vigilant anti-tank missiles**
U.K.

PLATE 78
**Shorland Armoured
Patrol Car, Mk 3**
U.K.

Land Rover transmission is via the four-speed gearbox and a two-speed transfer case to differentials on 'solid' axles at front and rear, with suspension consisting of semi-elliptic leaf springs controlled by hydraulic shock absorbers.

The Shorland's rectangular crew compartment has the driver at the right and the commander at the left in the British Army version, although these positions are reversed in left-hand drive models for export. There are separate windscreens for the driver and commander in the front plate of the hull and these can be covered by hinged drop-down bullet-proof visors incorporating laminated glass vision blocks. Observation hatches are provided in both side doors and at the rear of the crew compartment, the latter large enough to serve also as an escape hatch. The third crew member, the gunner, has a seat suspended from the turret ring as well as a fold-down seat for use when not on patrol. The turret, which is

located at the back of the roof of the crew compartment on the centre line, is similar to that of the Ferret Mark 2 Scout Car, the chief difference being that six smoke grenade dischargers are fitted, three either side, to Shorlands used by the British Army (on the Ferret the smoke dischargers are attached to the front of the hull). Early Shorlands did not have this fitment, which is optional for export models.

The standard armament is either a Browning 0.30-in machine gun or a 7.62-mm G.P.M.G., but a 38-mm tear gas projector or a water cannon can be fitted instead for special internal security duties. In the water-cannon role, a water-tank trailer equipped with an engine-driven pump and a hose connection to the water cannon is towed by the Shorland. The machine gun or other armament is mounted at the right-hand side of the turret face and is aimed by means of a periscopic sight on the turret roof. A small searchlight, mounted on the outside of the turret on the left-hand side, is linked with the armament. The interior of the Shorland's hull is lined with thick polyurethane foam faced with plastic sheeting, and there is an air conditioner and heating system. Two Vigilant anti-tank missile launchers were fitted experimentally to the Shorland but were not adopted in service. This version, which was standard in other respects, is shown in the upper illustration. At the extreme rear of the vehicle, in an armour-plated compartment rather like the boot of a passenger car, is the petrol tank and a spare wheel.

There are also several fully-armoured personnel carriers on the Land Rover chassis, some of which are marketed by the Armoured Vehicle Division of Ets. Beherman Demoen N.V./S.A. The Shorland SB.301, developed by Short Brothers and Harland Ltd. and sold to over a dozen countries, has been followed by the SB.401, similar in appearance but with the 91 h.p. V-8 Land Rover engine. Both types have fully-enclosed armoured bodies seating six personnel in addition to the driver and co-driver.

AT.104 Armoured Internal Security Vehicle Plates 79 and 80

Among the first vehicles to be specifically designed for urban internal security duties were two prototype armoured cars built as a commercial venture by GKN Sankey Ltd of Wellington, Shropshire in 1971 and 1972 respectively. The first was the AT.100, a fully armoured vehicle designed to carry 10 to 12 personnel. In order to

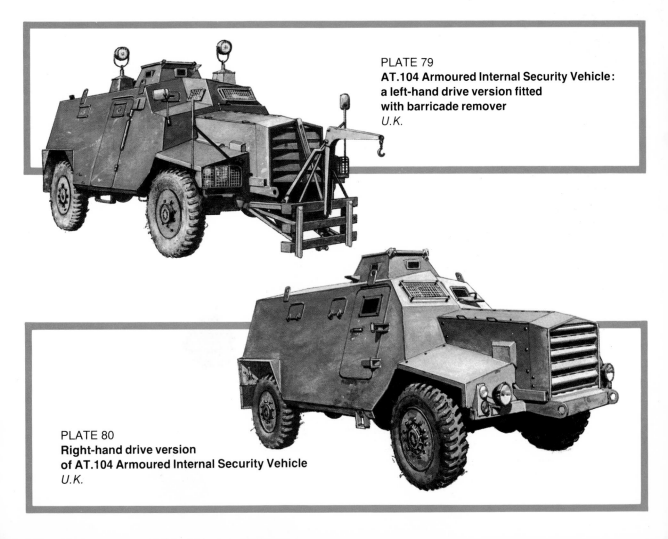

PLATE 79
AT.104 Armoured Internal Security Vehicle: a left-hand drive version fitted with barricade remover
U.K.

PLATE 80
Right-hand drive version of AT.104 Armoured Internal Security Vehicle
U.K.

cut down costs, the running gear and engine were taken from standard production line components of Bedford (the British division of General Motors) trucks. The AT.100 was a 4 × 2 forward control vehicle with a limited off-the-road performance which remained as a prototype only.

The second GKN Sankey internal security vehicle was the AT.104, with four-wheel drive and the engine in front of the driver. The layout of this model owed more to that of the Humber 1-ton Armoured 4 × 4 Truck (FV.1611) than to its predecessor. The Humber was still widely used by the British Army at the time and the production of its armoured hulls was shared by GKN Sankey and the Royal Ordnance Factories.

Although the AT.104 was less compact than the forward control AT.100, the two vehicles were generally similar in layout, with a half-cab for the driver on either the right or left side, according to the traffic system of the user country, and a roomy crew compartment behind. Unlike the AT.100, the AT.104 had a single slope for the hull sides so that a flat, instead of angled, door could be used on the side away from the driver. The driver's cab had a side door and access was also provided through the rear of the hull. Vision arrangements consisted of an armoured glass windscreen and two side windows (one of them in the cab door) for the driver, and drop-down armour plate hatches at the front of the hull (next to the driver's cab), the sides and at the rear. A square, non-rotating cupola for the vehicle commander was located on the hull roof on the centre line just behind the driver's cab. This had a roof hatch and armoured glass vision blocks on all sides. The hull was of all-welded steel construction, varying between 6 and 12.5 mm in thickness.

A choice of standard Bedford truck engines was offered for the AT.104, including the Models 330 and 466 six-cylinder diesels of around 100 h.p., which were recommended, or a six-cylinder petrol engine of 134 h.p. The Allison AT.540 four-speed automatic transmission was standardised because of the benefits it offered in emergency situations during security operations. The suspension consisted of semi-elliptic springs controlled by hydraulic shock absorbers.

Various optional fittings were available, including a machine gun turret or pintle mounting, smoke grenade dischargers, searchlights and a hydraulically operated winch and barricade remover. AT.104s have been supplied to the Dutch police (complete with the barricade removers) and the Brunei army.

AT.104 Armoured Internal Security Vehicle showing side weapon ports open and wire grilles protecting driver's front and side windows

AT.105 Armoured Internal Security Vehicle Plates 81 and 82

Claimed to be the first vehicle specifically designed for a paramilitary internal security role, its predecessors having more limited functions, the AT.105 is a logical development of the AT.104. Combining the best features of the AT.104 with the more compact forward control layout which offers better protection for the engine as well as better vision for the driver, the AT.105 first appeared in 1974.

Bedford lorry components are once again used to minimise costs, this time employing as standard the Model 500 six-cylinder engine developing 147 h.p. at 2,800 r.p.m. However, the Rolls-Royce B.81 eight-cylinder petrol engine, giving 164 h.p. at 3,000 r.p.m. is offered as an alternative, a possible inducement to countries already equipped with vehicles having engines in the Rolls-Royce military range. The engine is linked, as in the AT.104, to the Allison AT.540 automatic gearbox, and the suspension is similar to that of the earlier vehicle. The tyres are the 12.00 × 20 'run-flat' type.

The armoured hull of the AT.105, although similar in general configuration to that of the AT.104, has been redesigned to give better protection against mine explosions under the vehicle, the underside being a pronounced V-shape to deflect blasts. The welded-steel armour plate has a maximum thickness of 16 mm at the sides, a significant advance over the 12.5-mm maximum of the earlier GKN Sankey internal security vehicles.

The AT.105 carries 10 personnel: the driver at the front in a left-hand or right-hand cab next to the engine, as required by the user country, the commander behind him in approximately the centre of the hull, and eight personnel on longitu-

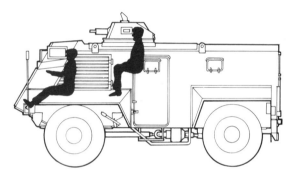

AT.105

AT.105 Armoured Internal Security Vehicle. This version is equipped with a twin 7.62-mm machine-gun turret

dinal seats facing each other, four on each side. There are single doors in the centre of the hull on each side and twin doors at the rear. There are seven vision hatches, which can also be used as firing ports, in the hull, one at the front, between the driver and the engine, four in the sides and two in the rear doors.

In the standard version of the AT.105 the vehicle commander has a square cupola with armoured vision blocks on all four sides, but this can be replaced by one of a range of turrets equipped with one or two 7.62-mm machine guns, a 20-mm cannon, or a 75-mm gun in a turret like that of the Scorpion light tank.

PLATE 81
AT.105 Armoured Internal Security Vehicle
U.K.

PLATE 82
AT.105 fitted with twin 7.62-mm M.G. turret
U.K.

United States of America

Car, Armored, Light 4 × 4, Commando
Plates 83 and 84

Relatively few wheeled armoured vehicles have been built in the United States, even experimentally, since World War 2. However, Commando, a private venture by the Cadillac Gage Company, has enjoyed great succcess and been bought by over 20 countries, in addition to being the only major wheeled armoured vehicle used by the U.S. forces.

PLATE 83
**U.S. police version
of Commando V.150**
U.S.A.

PLATE 84
**Commando V.150 in
76-mm gun version**
U.S.A.

Arising from experiments conducted by Cadillac Gage in the early 1960s with armoured bodies on truck chassis, the prototype Commando was completed in March 1963. It was given extensive trials in various countries with differing climatic conditions and production of the first Commando V-100s started at the beginning of 1964. At this time, the United States became involved in the war in Vietnam and some of the first Commandos completed were supplied to the South Vietnamese army. Later, the U.S. forces themselves used the Commando in Vietnam.

The Commando has a ballistically well-shaped single-piece welded hull. The engine is located at the rear left-hand side and transmits the power through a transfer box and drive shafts (protected by the armoured hull) through lockable differentials on 'solid' front and rear axles. The wheels are fitted with large section 'run-flat' type tyres and the suspension is of the leaf spring variety with shock absorbers at each wheel station. There is a high ground clearance of between 0.381 and 0.431 metres, according to model. The hull is waterproofed and the Commando can enter water

Commando V-150S with 25-mm gun turret

without special preparation and travel at up to
4.8 km/h, being propelled by its wheels. The
engine in the Commando V-100 is a Chrysler 361
V-8 petrol model developing 210 h.p. This has
the advantage of being similar to that of the
widely used M113 armoured personnel carrier.
The later V-150 also uses the Chrysler petrol
engine but can have as an alternative a Cummins
V-6 diesel developing 155 h.p. at 3,300 r.p.m.
The larger and heavier Commando V-200 has a
275-h.p. Chrysler 440 diesel. The maximum
speed for all models is about 96 km/h.

The Commando was designed as a multipurpose armoured car and in its standard versions
can act as a personnel carrier (without a turret and
carrying up to 12 troops), convoy escort vehicle,
patrol or reconnaissance car, or internal security
vehicle. The turret can mount twin 7.62-mm
machine guns, one 12.7-mm and one 7.62-mm
machine guns, a 76-mm gun, a Mecar 90-mm gun
turret or either a 20- or 25-mm Oerlikon cannon.
The G.E.C. 7.62-mm six-barrelled minigun is
another turret alternative for all models, and
Dragon or TOW anti-tank launchers can be
added.

Special versions include: command, communications or police models in which a pod
attachment raises the centre part of the hull roof;
a Lance missile carrier; an 81-mm mortar carrier;
and a recovery vehicle. The latter is equipped
with an A-frame jib (which folds back over the
rear hull when not in use) and a recovery winch
mounted in the nose. All Commando models,
incidentally, carry a winch for self-recovery if
bogged down.

The V-100 Commando with Browning turret is
employed by the U.S. Army where it is designated M706; The U.S. Air Force has a model
with a fixed superstructure on which up to three
machine guns can be mounted on pintles. In
addition, various models of Commando are in
service with the armed forces or police of more
than 20 different countries.

Cadillac Gage Commando Scout (Light Reconnaissance Car) Plates 85 and 86

Seeking to emulate, with a smaller armoured car,
the commercial success of their Commando V-

100, V-150 and V-200 armoured cars, the Cadillac
Gage company has produced, in the Scout, what
is in some ways a more sophisticated vehicle than
the earlier products.

The Scout, or Commando Scout to give it its
full title, is basically a two-man reconnaissance car
approximately the size of the British Fox. The
hull is made of welded steel plates at angles
intended to give the optimum protection for their
thickness; the glacis plate is a single slope at about
12 degrees from the horizontal from the nose to
just in front of the turret base. Under this are
accommodated the driver, at the left, and the
engine. As well as giving ballistic protection, the
knife edge angle of glacis and nose plates is
intended as a means of cutting through under-
growth and other obstacles. The driver's hatch,
which incorporates a wide glass vision block at the
front only, slides forward down the glacis plate
both to give direct open driving vision and to
provide access to the vehicle. There is also a door
in the rear of the hull. The one-man turret, fitted
in most versions, is located immediately behind
the driver on the centre line and over the rear
wheels. A dome-shaped cupola on the turret roof
is equipped with eight vision blocks, giving all
round observation, and a periscope. A semi-
circular hatch for the commander/gunner provides rear protection for him when it is raised.
The turret has power traverse and several main
armament alternatives: twin 7.62-mm machine
guns, one 7.62-mm and one 12.7-mm machine
guns, a 40-mm grenade launcher, a 20-mm cannon, or a 30-mm cannon.

Versions of the Scout without a turret are for
the TOW wire-guided anti-tank missile launcher,
the 106-mm recoilless rifle (both carried on a
square superstructure) and a command vehicle.
The latter has a rectangular 'pod' in place of the
turret, with vision blocks on all four sides and on
which a machine gun can be carried on a pintle
mounting. This version has provision for command radio equipment and normally carries a
crew of three.

The engine of the Commando Scout is a compact V-6 Cummins diesel developing 155 h.p.
The transmission is an Allison automatic four-
speed gearbox. The front axle is 'solid', carried on
parallel arms with coil springs, whereas the rear

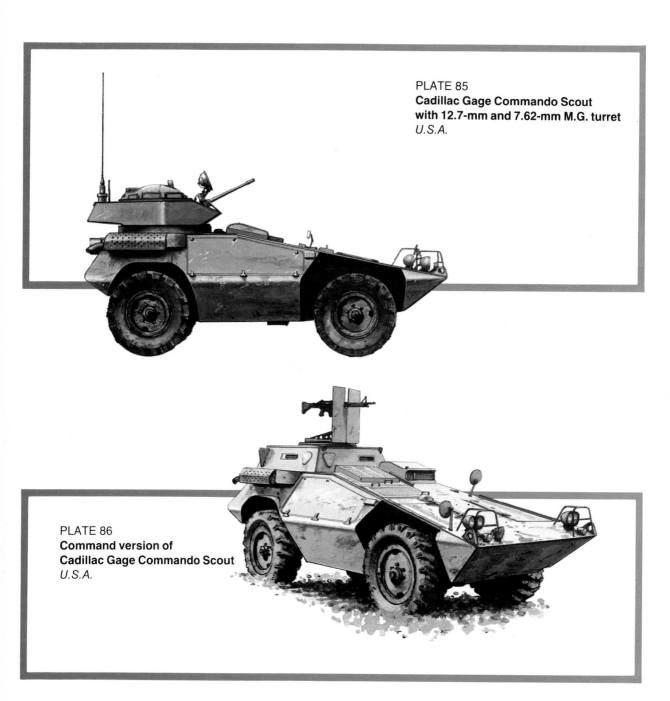

PLATE 85
**Cadillac Gage Commando Scout
with 12.7-mm and 7.62-mm M.G. turret**
U.S.A.

PLATE 86
**Command version of
Cadillac Gage Commando Scout**
U.S.A.

wheels are independently sprung, also with coil springs. There are shock absorbers at each wheel station and the wheels, large for the size of the vehicle, are fitted with 15.5 × 21 tubeless 'run-flat' tyres. Both front and rear differentials are lockable and, with low ground pressure and provision for a high degree of vertical wheel movement, an excellent cross-country performance is claimed for the Scout. Maximum road speed is 97 km/h and the range is 800 km. There is no provision for swimming but the maximum fording depth is 1.16 metres.

Details of any overseas sales of the Commando Scout are not available at the time of writing, although it seems likely that at least some of the countries already operating the Commando (V-100, V-150 or V-200) will also purchase the Scout as a complementary vehicle for short range reconnaissance or allied tasks.

Cadillac Gage Commando Scout command vehicle with 12.7-mm machine gun

Zimbabwe/South Africa

Hippo and Crocodile Armoured
Personnel Carriers Plates 87 and 88

The military activities in Rhodesia (now Zimbabwe) between 1972 and 1979 resulted in a proliferation of armoured or protected vehicles of various kinds. The main need at first was for protection against land mines, both for soldiers and civilians. Various vehicles, ranging from Land Rovers to five-ton trucks were adapted to shield their crews from mine blasts. This protection usually took the form of a special compartment with a V-shaped underside, to deflect blasts, in which the driver and crew were seated high in the vehicle. In some models the body was placed well above the chassis components, which were modified with extended steering columns, etc. The high centre of gravity in most of these vehicles reduced their stability, and roll bars were almost universally fitted to protect the crew if they overturned, whether through accident or mine explosion. The extra weight imposed on the chassis used was sometimes lessened by leaving the engine unprotected in early vehicles. Heavy conveyer belting, used in mines, which has a fair degree of shock and bullet resistance, was sometimes used to supplement the steel protection.

Two further means of mitigating the effect of exploding mines were to partly fill the tyres with water (this dampened down the movement) and to fit wheel-attachment bolts that would shear easily. This made it easier to fit a replacement wheel quickly using fresh bolts. In later vehicles, more attention was given to protection against small arms fire, and the side armour was raised.

Some vehicles of this kind, such as the Land Rover-based 'Ojay', were made available commercially and were used by farmers and other civilians for travelling on roads likely to be mined. However, two types of armoured vehicles used mainly by the military and security forces in Zimbabwe are shown here.

The Hippo is of South African origin (and is used widely in South Africa) and is based on a British Bedford model MK series 4 × 4 chassis (four-ton military rating) with a six-cylinder engine developing 102 h.p. at 2,800 r.p.m. This vehicle has accommodation for about 10 personnel (seated on longitudinal benches facing outwards) in addition to the driver on the right-hand side and the vehicle commander on the left. The hull is V-shaped in section with supplementary protection on the sides. There is an armoured glass divided windscreen at the front and five armoured glass windows, divided only by narrow bars, on each side giving very good protected vision for all the crew. There are two roll bars over the rear compartment. The engine compartment is not armoured and its top is covered by a canvas cover only.

The Crocodile, built in Rhodesia (now Zimbabwe), is a more modern version of the Hippo and is in appearance more akin to a conventional military wheeled armoured personnel carrier, albeit like a design of the 1950s. It does, in fact, strongly resemble the Swedish Terrängbil m/42 KP, a vehicle designed in 1944 but used by the Swedish contingent of the United Nations force in the Congo in the early 1960s and elsewhere. The chassis used for the Crocodile is that of the Japanese Nissan five-ton long-wheelbase commercial lorry which, although well able to carry the armoured hull, has limited cross-country performance because of its 4 × 2 drive. An alternative to the Nissan chassis is the Isuzu which is of similar capacity and performance. The armoured hull, behind the engine, is in one piece, the lower half sloping inwards to a V-shape. The upper half of the hull also slopes inwards to an open roof, protected by three roll bars. There are eight weapons ports in each side of the upper hull and two in the doors at the rear. There is a large bullet-proof glass windscreen for the driver on the right-hand side of the sloping front plate of the hull and a smaller one for the co-driver. The latter's window also has a hinged steel flap. There are large hatches in the hull either side of the driving compartment. The Crocodile version shown here can carry 18 personnel including the driver, those in the back sitting on longitudinal benches facing outwards.

There are other vehicles similar in size and function to the Crocodile, such as the Puma, some having separate one-man cabs and others with forward control. There are also load carriers with only the cab armoured. The army also developed several smaller types of vehicles, similar in general configuration to Crocodile, but using Mercedes-Benz Unimog 4 × 4 chassis.

PLATE 87
Crocodile
ZIMBABWE

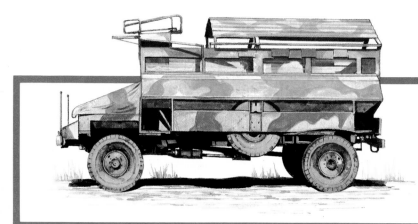

PLATE 88
Hippo
ZIMBABWE/SOUTH AFRICA

Type	Wheel configuration	Weight (tonnes)	Length (m)	Width (m)	Height (m)	Max armour (mm)	Armament	Engine	h.p.	Max speed (km/h) road	Max speed (km/h) water	Road range (km)	Crew	Notes
Belgium														
AB FN type G (90 mm)	4×4	8.3	4.47	2.2	2.52	13	1×90 mm, 1×7.62 mm M.G.	FN 652 6 cyl.	130	110	—	600	3	Length including gun 5.42 m
AB FN type G (60 mm mortier)	4×4	7.4	4.47	2.2	2.37	13	1×60 mm mortar, 2×7.62 mm M.G.	FN 652 6 cyl.	130	110	—	600	3	
Brazil														
EE-11 Urutu	6×6	11	6	2.66	2.66	12	1×12.7 mm M.G.	Mercedes Benz OM 352A 6 cyl. diesel	172	90	12	600	15	
EE-9 Cascavel	6×6	10.8	5.15	2.66	2.62	12	1×90 mm, 1×7.62 mm M.G.	Mercedes Benz OM 352A 6 cyl. diesel	172	100	—	750	3	Length excludes gun
EE-17 Sucuri	6×6	18.5	6.3	2.6	2.8		1×105 mm, 1×7.62 mm M.G.	Detroit Diesel 6V53T 6 cyl.	300	110	—	600	3	
EE-3 Jararaca	4×4	3.765	3.9	2	1.28		1×12.7 mm M.G.	Mercedes Benz OM 314 4 cyl. diesel	102	110	—	600	3	
Canada/Switzerland														
A.V.G.P. Grizzly	6×6	10.5	5.97	2.5	2.53		1×12.7 mm, 1×7.62 mm M.G.	Detroit Diesel 6V53T 6 cyl.	275	100	10.5	600	11	
A.V.G.P. Cougar	6×6	10.5	5.97	2.5	2.62		1×76 mm, 1×7.62 mm M.G.	Detroit Diesel 6V53T 6 cyl.	275	100	10.5	600	3	
A.V.G.P. Husky	6×6	10.5	5.97	2.5	2.64		1×7.62 mm M.G.	Detroit Diesel 6V53T 6 cyl.	275	100	10.5	600	4	Length excludes crane
Czechoslovakia														
PL dv K 30-mm	6×6	9.5	6.984	2.41	3.06	10	2×30 mm M53	Tatra T912-2 6 cyl. diesel	110	60	—	500	3	
122-mm rocket launcher on Tatra 813	8×8	19	N.D.	N.D.	N.D.	N.D.	40×122 mm BM21 (+40 reloads)	Tatra T930 12 cyl. diesel	270	80	—	650	4	
OT-64 (SKOT)	8×8	14.5	7.4	2.5	2.7	10	1×14.5 mm, 1×7.62 mm M.G.	Tatra T928 8 cyl. diesel	180	94	9	710	2+15	Developed in conjunction with Poland. Data is for SKOT-2A
Egypt														
Walid A.P.C.	4×4	N.D.	N.D.	N.D.	N.D.	N.D.	1×7.62 mm M.G.	Deutz diesel	N.D.	N.D.	—	N.D.	10	Length including gun (FL-11 turret) is 6.15 m

Type	Wheel configuration	Weight (tonnes)	Length (m)	Width (m)	Height (m)	Max armour (mm)	Armament	Engine	h.p.	Max speed (km/h) road	Max speed (km/h) water	Road range (km)	Crew	Notes
France														
EBR-75	8×8	13.5	5.56	2.42	2.32	40	1×75 mm, 1×7.62 mm M.G.	Panhard 12 cyl.	200	100	—	650	4	2 extra M.G. in hull not always fitted
EBR-ETT	8×8	13	5.21	2.44				Panhard 12 cyl.	200	100	—	650	3+12	
AML HE 60–7	4×4	4.5	3.765	1.915	1.865	12	1×60 mm mortar, 2×7.62 mm M.G.	Panhard 4 HD 4 cyl.	90	100	—	600	3	
AML H-90	4×4	5.5	3.79	1.97	2.07	12	1×90 mm, 1×7.62 mm M.G.	Panhard 4 HD 4 cyl.	90	100	—	600	3	Length including gun is 5.11 m
VTT M-3	4×4	6.1	4.45	2.4	2	12	See text	Panhard 4 HD 4 cyl.	90	100	4	600	2+10	
ERC-90S Sagaie	6×6	7.4	5.02	2.5	2.24	N.D.	1×90 mm, 1×7.62 mm M.G.	Peugeot PRV-V6 6 cyl.	140	110	9	950	3	Length including gun is 7.78 m
ERC-90 Lynx	6×6	7	5.12	2.5	2.13	N.D.	1×90 mm, 1×7.62 mm M.G.	Peugeot PRV-V6 6 cyl.	140	110	9	950	3	Length including gun is 5.95 m
VCR-TT	6×6	7	4.57	2.5	2.53	N.D.	1×7.62 mm M.G.	Peugeot PRV-V6 6 cyl.	140	110	9	950	12	
VAB (Renault) (4×4)	4×4	13	5.855	2.48	2.06		See text	Saviem-MAN D2356 HM 72 6 cyl. diesel	220	92	7	1300	12	Height is to hull top
VAB (Renault) (6×6)	6×6	14	5.855	2.48	2.06		See text	Saviem-MAN D2356 HM 72 6 cyl. diesel	220	92	7	1100	12	Height is to hull top
Crotale (acquisition unit)	4×4	12.5	6.22	2.65	2.04	5	—	ACEC electric transmission		70	—	500	3	
Crotale (firing unit)	4×4	14.8	6.22	2.65	2.04	5	4×missiles	ACEC electric transmission		70	—	500	3	
Berliet VXB-170	4×4	12.7	5.99	2.5	2.05		See text	Berliet 8 cyl. diesel	170	85	5	750	12–15	
AMX-10 RC	6×6	15.8	6.243	2.84	2.565		1×105 mm, 1×7.62 mm M.G.	Hispano-Suiza HS115 8 cyl. diesel	280	85	7.2	800	4	Length including gun is 9.13 m
Germany, Democratic Republic														
SK-1	4×4	5.4	4	2	2.8	8	1×7.92 mm M.G.	Robur 4 cyl.	55	80	—	350	5	
SK-2	6×6	9.1	7.5	2.5	4.3	N.D.	1 water cannon	Horch 6 cyl. diesel	120	48	—	585	3	
Germany, Federal Republic														
Transportpanzer 1	6×6	15.9	6.76	2.98	2.3	N.D.	1×20 mm or 1×7.62 mm M.G.	Daimler Benz OM-402A 8 cyl.	320	90	10	800	2+10	Height is to hull top
APE	4×4	14.5	6.93	3.08	2.4	N.D.	1×20 mm or 1×7.62 mm M.G.	Daimler Benz OM-402A 8 cyl. diesel	320	80	12	800	2+10–12	Height is to hull top
Spähpanzer 2 Luchs	8×8	19.5	7.743	2.98	2.84	N.D.	1×20 mm Rh 202, 1×7.62 mm M.G.	Daimler Benz OM-403VA 10 cyl. diesel	390	90	10	800	4	

Vehicle	Config.						Armament	Engine						Remarks
Transportpanzer UR-416	4×4	6.3	4.99	2.26	2.24	9	See text	Daimler Benz OM-352 6 cyl. diesel	110	80	—	700	2+8	
Hungary														
FUG (OT 65)	4×4	6.1	5.79	2.362	1.91	10	1×7.62 mm M.G.	Csepel D-414.44 4 cyl. diesel	100	87	9	500	2+3	Has 4 auxiliary wheels
FUG-70 (OT 66)	4×4	7	5.79	2.362	2.525	10	1×14.5 mm, 1×7.62 mm M.G.	Raba-MAN D-2156 6 cyl. diesel	120	100	10	500	3+6	No auxiliary wheels
Irish Republic/Belgium														
Timoney-BDX A.P.C.	4×4	9.35	5.3	2.5	2.12	12.7	See text	Chrysler 360 CID 8 cyl.	200	100	—	500	10	Height is to hull top
Israel														
Ram V-1	4×4	3.6	5.02	2.03	1.71	10	1-4 × 7.62 mm M.G.	Dodge 225-2 6 cyl.	120	95	—	850	2+6	
Italy														
Fiat 6614 A.P.C.	4×4	8.5	5.86	2.5	1.78	8	1×12.7 mm M.G.	Fiat 8062.24 6 cyl. diesel	160	96	4.5	700	11	
Fiat 6616 Armoured Car	4×4	7.95	5.37	2.5	2.035	8	1×20 mm Rh 202, 1×7.62 mm M.G.	Fiat 8062.24 6 cyl. diesel	160	100	5	750	3	Height is to turret top
Netherlands														
PWI YP-408	8×6	12	6.23	2.4	2.37	15	1×12.7 mm M.G.	DAF DS-575 6 cyl. diesel	165	80	—	500	2+10	Data is for PWI-S(GR)
South Africa														
Ratel A.P.C.	6×6	16	N.D.	N.D.	N.D.	N.D.	1×20 mm, 1×7.62 mm M.G.	N.D. (diesel)	N.D.	105	—	N.D.	10	
U.S.S.R														
BTR-152	6×6	8.95	6.83	2.32	2.05	13.5	1×M.G. (7.62/12.7/14.5 mm)	ZIS-123 6 cyl.	110	75	—	650	2+17	
BTR-60 PB	8×8	10.3	7.56	2.825	2.31	14	1×14.5 mm, 1×7.62 mm M.G.	2×GAZ-49 B 12 cyl. (total)	180	80	10	—	2+14	
BTR-40	4×4	5.3	5	1.9	1.75	8		GAZ-40 6 cyl.	80	80	—	285	2+8	
BTR-40A/ZPU	4×4	5.95	5	1.9	2.5	8	2×14.5 mm M.G. (A.A.)	GAZ-40 6 cyl.	80	80	—	285	4	
BRDM	4×4	5.6	5.7	2.225	1.9	10	1×7.62 mm M.G.	GAZ-40P 6 cyl.	90	80	9	500	5	
BRDM with AT-1 Snapper	4×4	5.6	5.7	2.225	N.D.	10	3×AT-1 missiles	GAZ-40P 6 cyl.	90	80	9	500	2	
BRDM with AT-2 Swatter	4×4	5.6	5.7	2.225	N.D.	10	4×AT-2 missiles	GAZ-40P 6 cyl.	90	80	9	500	2	
BRDM-2	4×4	7	5.75	2.35	2.31	10	1×14.5 mm 1×7.62 mm M.G.	GAZ-41 8 cyl.	140	100	10	750	4	
BRDM-2 with AT-3 Sagger	4×4	7	5.75	2.35	2.01	10	6×AT-3 missiles +8 reserves	GAZ-41 8 cyl.	140	100	10	750	2	
BRDM-3 with AT-5 Spandrel	4×4	N.D.	5.75	2.35	N.D.	N.D.	5×AT-5 missiles	GAZ (?)	N.D.	N.D.	N.D.	N.D.	N.D.	
SA-9 Gaskin on BRDM-2	4×4	7	5.75	2.35	2.9	10	4×SA-9 missiles +4 (?) reserves	GAZ-41 8 cyl.	140	100	10	750	3	

Type	Wheel configuration	Weight (tonnes)	Length (m)	Width (m)	Height (m)	Max armour (mm)	Armament	Engine	h.p.	Max speed (km/h) road	water	Road range (km)	Crew	Notes
SA-8 Gecko	6×6	N.D.	9.1	2.9	4.1	N.D.	4×SA-8 missiles	2×ZIL 16 cyl. (total)	360	N.D.	?	N.D.	4	See footnote
Frog-7	8×8	20	10.75	2.8	3.66	N.D.	1×FROG 7 missile	2×ZIL 375 16 cyl. (total)	360	65	—	N.D.	5	See footnote
SS-1C Scud B	8×8	28	13.56	3	3.8	N.D.	1×SS-1C missile	D-12-A-375 12 cyl. diesel	375	55	—	N.D.	5	
SS-12 Scaleboard	8×8	28	13.58	3	3.7	N.D.	1×SS-12 missile	D-12-A-375 12 cyl. diesel	375	55	—	N.D.	5	
U.K.														
Scout Car, Ferret Mk1/2	4×4	4.37	3.835	1.905	1.651	16	1×7.62 mm M.G.	Rolls-Royce B.60 Mk 6A 6 cyl.	129	93	—	300	3	
Scout Car, Ferret Mk 2	4×4	4.39	3.835	1.905	1.879	16	1×7.62 mm M.G.	Rolls-Royce B.60 Mk 6A 6 cyl.	129	93	—	300	2	
Scout Car, Ferret Mk 4	4×4	5.4	3.962	2.133	2.336	16	1×7.62 mm M.G.	Rolls-Royce B.60 Mk 6A 6 cyl.	129	80	3.8	300	2	
Scout Car, Ferret Mk 5	4×4	5.89	3.962	2.133	2.044	16	1×7.62 mm 4×Swingfire	Rolls-Royce B.60 Mk 6A 6 cyl.	129	80	3.8	300	2	
CVR (W) Fox	4×4	6.386	4.242	2.134	2.2	N.D.	1×30 mm, 1×7.62 mm M.G.	Jaguar XK 6 cyl.	195	104	5		3	Length including gun is 5.359 m
Armoured Car, Saladin Mk 2.	6×6	11.59	4.93	2.54	2.39	32	1×76 mm, 1×7.62 mm M.G.	Rolls-Royce B.80 8 cyl.	160	72	—	400	3	Length including gun is 5.384 m
Carrier, Personnel, Saracen Mk 2	6×6	10.17	5.233	2.539	2.463	16	1×7.62 mm M.G.	Rolls-Royce B.80 8 cyl.	160	72	—	400	2+10	
Truck, Armoured, 1-ton Humber	4×4	7.55	4.926	2.044	2.12	N.D.		Rolls-Royce B.60 Mk 6A 6 cyl.	120	60	—	400	2+6–8	
Shorland (Mk 3)	4×4	3.543	4.292	1.764	2.159	8.25	1×7.62 mm M.G.	Rover 6 cyl.	91	88	—	257	3	
AT.104	4×4	8.9	5.486	2.438	2.489	12.5		Bedford 6 cyl. diesel	98	80	—	640	2+9	Alternative engines available
AT.105	4×4	9.144	5.17	2.489	2.59	16		Bedford Model 500	147	88	—	640	2+8	
U.S.A														
Car, Armored, Commando	4×4	7.37	5.689	2.26	2.438	N.D.	2×7.62 mm M.G.	Chrysler 361 8 cyl.	210	100	4.8	500	12	Data for V-100, typical armament
Commando Scout	4×4	6.123	4.7	2.16	2.06	N.D.	2×7.62 mm M.G.	Cummins 6 cyl. diesel	155	97	—	800	2	Typical armament
Zimbabwe/South Africa														
Hippo A.P.C.	4×4	N.D.	N.D.	N.D.	N.D.	N.D.	—	Bedford 6 cyl.	102	N.D.	—	N.D.	2+10	Wheel base is 3.96 m
Crocodile A.P.C.	4×4	N.D.	N.D.	N.D.	N.D.	N.D.	—	Isuzu or Nissan	N.D.	N.D.	—	N.D.	18	

—: not applicable; N.D.: no data available; Note: the Soviet Likhachev Automobile Plant, Moscow, ZIL, was formerly designated ZIS

Index